THE OPEN UNIVERSITY
A SCIENCE FOUNDATION COURSE

G000136795

UNIT 22 BIOCHEMISTRY

THE SCIENCE FOUNDATION COURSE TEAM

Geoff Brown (Earth Sciences)
Jim Burge (BBC)
Neil Chalmers (Biology)
Bob Cordell (Biology, General Editor)
Pauline Corfield (Assessment Group and
    Summer School Group)
Debbie Crouch (Designer)
Sue Dobson (Illustrator)
Dee Edwards (Earth Sciences; S101 Evaluation)
Graham Farmelo (Chairman)
John Greenwood (Librarian)
Mike Gunton (BBC)
Charles Harding (Chemistry)
Robin Harding (Biology)
Nigel Harris (Earth Sciences, General Editor)
Linda Hodgkinson (Course Coordinator)
David Jackson (BBC)
David Johnson (Chemistry, General Editor)
Tony Jolly (BBC, Series Producer)
Ken Kirby (BBC)
Perry Morley (Editor)
Peter Morrod (Chemistry)
Pam Owen (Illustrator)
Rissa de la Paz (BBC)
Julia Powell (Editor)
David Roberts (Chemistry)
David Robinson (Biology)
Shelagh Ross (Physics, General Editor)
Dick Sharp (Editor)

Ted Smith (BBC)
Margaret Swithenby (Editor)
Nick Watson (BBC)
Dave Williams (Earth Sciences)
Geoff Yarwood (Earth Sciences)

Consultants: Keith Hodgkinson (Physics)
Judith Metcalfe (Biology)
Pat Murphy (Biology)
Irene Ridge (Biology)
Jonathan Silvertown (Biology)

External assessor: F. J. Vine FRS

Others whose S101 contribution has been of
considerable value in the preparation of S102:

Stuart Freake (Physics)
Anna Furth (Biology)
Stephen Hurry (Biology)
Jane Nelson (Chemistry)
Mike Pentz (Chairman and General Editor, S101)
Milo Shott (Physics)
Russell Stannard (Physics)
Steve Swithenby (Physics)
Peggy Varley (Biology)
Kiki Warr (Chemistry)
Chris Wilson (Earth Sciences)

The illustration on the front cover shows a desert locust—heterotroph feeds on autotroph. (Reproduced by permission of David Robinson.)

The Open University, Walton Hall, Milton Keynes, MK7 6AA.

First published 1988. Reprinted 1989.

Copyright © 1988, 1989 The Open University.

Designed by the Graphic Design Group of the Open University.
Filmset by Santype International Limited, Salisbury, Wiltshire, printed by Thomson Litho, East Kilbride, Scotland.

ISBN 0 335 16336 X

The text forms part of an Open University Course. For general availability of supporting material referred to in this text please write to: Open University Educational Enterprises Limited, 12 Cofferidge Close, Stony Stratford, Milton Keynes, MK11 1BY, Great Britain.

Further information on Open University Courses may be obtained from the Admissions Office, The Open University, P.O. Box 48, Walton Hall, Milton Keynes, MK7 6AB.

1.2

BIOCHEMISTRY

PHYSIOLOGY

RESPIRATION

BIOSYNTHESIS

STUDY GUIDE

Unit 22 consists of the text, an AV sequence, a TV programme and an experiment. The whole Unit is one-and-a-half weeks' work. You should aim to read to the end of Section 3 in the study week for Unit 21, and then to study Sections 4 to 8 in the week set aside for Unit 22.

Section 4.6 includes an experiment on enzymes that uses arrowroot. This is a kind of starch that is sold in almost all chemist's shops. Buy some if you have not already done so. *The day before you do the experiment, you should make up the solution of arrowroot*: follow the instructions for solution 1 in Part A of the Experimental Procedure (p. 34). Once you have made this solution and allowed it to cool, the experiment itself should not take more than about 45 minutes.

Although the TV programme can be viewed at any stage, you will find it provides a useful introduction to biochemistry and is therefore worth seeing early on. However, you should read the TV notes (Section 9) before watching it.

> It is MOST important that you study the AV sequence associated with Section 6.2 while you are reading that Section. Section 6.2 is in many ways the core of the Unit, and it is incomprehensible without the tape.

At the back of this book, there are a number of Colour Plates and electron micrographs, which serve to illustrate some important points covered in the text.

I INTRODUCTION

This Unit and the next explore two closely connected areas of biology—biochemistry and physiology. In the last three Units you have studied evolution, inheritance and cell division. You learned that evolution is a process that depends on the survival of the fittest offspring. You learned also that each individual begins life as a zygote and that this single cell divides repeatedly by mitosis. Eventually, after a period of growth and development, the individual becomes a sexually mature adult. It is during this period of growth from zygote to adult that so much death—and hence so much selection—occurs. Put another way, only those that grow and survive long enough to breed are successful in evolutionary terms. These simple but essential points are summarized in Figure 1 (overleaf).

Thus growth and survival are crucial to the continuation of life, and how organisms manage in these respects depends on their **biochemistry** and **physiology.** Though this Unit is primarily about biochemistry, it will help put this rather 'chemical' branch of biology in perspective if you note how it relates to physiology—the topic of the next Unit. Biochemistry is about the chemical and physical processes that go on within the cells of organisms. Two important examples are: **respiration**, the oxidation of organic compounds to provide energy; and **biosynthesis**, the synthesis of the substances of which organisms are made. Physiology is about the way groups of cells (tissues and organs) work together in an organized way, and also about the chemical and physical relationships an organism has with its environment.

The link between physiology and biochemistry is plain if you reflect on a few examples. Cells oxidize organic fuels to provide energy for numerous vital processes but, of course, the cells have to be supplied with the oxygen and with the organic fuels before they can do these oxidations. The details of cell respiration are part of *biochemistry*, and involve chemical reactions that take place in various parts of a cell. The subcellular components introduced in Unit 19—such as the cytosol, mitochondria and cell membranes—are the battlegrounds of biochemical change. In contrast, how organisms

MAINTENANCE

TURNOVER

PROTEIN HALF-LIFE

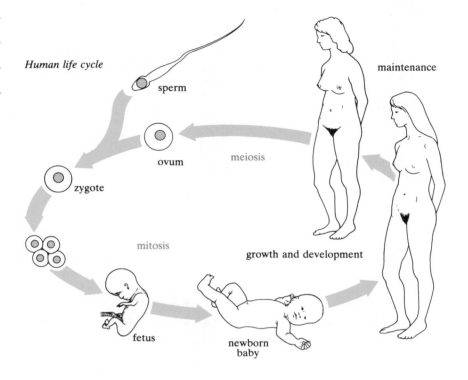

Human life cycle

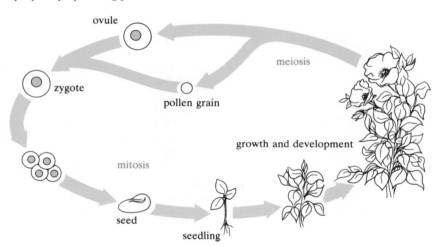

Life cycle of a flowering plant

FIGURE 1 Each generation in animals and plants involves growth to adulthood and reproduction.

obtain organic fuels and other nutrients from the environment and transport them to the biochemically active cells is part of *physiology*. Depending on whether the organism is, say, a fish, bird, or frog, physiological details vary; for example, whether they obtain their oxygen through gills, lungs or their skin. Though there are also some differences in biochemistry between one species and another, it is the similarities that are most striking. We shall focus, in this Unit, on the underlying unity of biochemistry, paying particular attention to growth and survival—the biological phenomena that connect us most strongly with the ideas of evolution discussed earlier.

Section 2 examines the biochemical processes involved in growth and survival—processes involved in the life cycle of all organisms. To take this further, you need to know more about the substances involved in cell structure and function, and these are covered in Sections 3 and 4. Finally, building on the material in these earlier Sections, Sections 5 to 8 explore in more detail the biochemical events within cells. Throughout the Unit, the aim is to relate what is happening to molecules inside cells to the more obvious day-to-day events in the lives of whole organisms.

2 GROWTH AND SURVIVAL

By survival we mean 'keeping alive'. Consider the growth of an organism from zygote to adult. The length of a generation varies from species to species: 3–4 weeks in the case of *Drosophila* to a hundred years or more in the types of bamboo mentioned in Unit 19. However, in all multicellular organisms the journey from zygote to adult involves making more cells (of the order of 10^{13} in a human adult) and, consequently, more chemicals of which the cells are made. But, besides this rather obvious kind of growth, there is another rather imperceptible process that is akin to growth. This is the synthesis of new cell chemicals, and often new cells as well, that is involved in the **maintenance** of an individual both during the period of growing up and in its adult stage.

In everyday conversation, parents will say of their teenage child, 'Oh, Mary's finished growing now' or 'We don't think John's going to get any taller'. And, of course, they are broadly right as regards external dimensions. However, in all organisms, the chemicals within cells and often the cells themselves are continuously being broken down and replaced. For example, the proteins of your tissues are all the time being broken down and replaced by newly biosynthesized molecules. This breaking down and replacement is referred to as **turnover**, and the rate of turnover of body protein is described in terms of the protein's **half-life**. Experiments using isotopically labelled amino acids show, for example, that half the protein of your liver is replaced every 10 days, and half the protein of your muscle every 160 days. Although other parts of you are turned over more slowly— for example, the proteins in the living core of your teeth—the fact is that turnover of protein and, indeed, of all other compounds in the body occurs continuously. The fabric of you as you sit before this page is, atom for atom, substantially different from the person of your name who existed a year ago.

Look again at Figure 1: the ideas of 'getting bigger' growth and maintenance growth should be pretty clear. But what does growth of either kind mean in chemical terms? Making new cell chemicals requires the following:

(a) a plan of what should be made;
(b) chemical raw materials from which the cell molecules can be constructed;
(c) a source of energy.

It would be wrong to regard these as three separate components in the synthesis of cell chemicals because they are all interrelated, as you will see. However, just as building a house depends on the architect's blueprint, on the availability of bricks and mortar and on the labour of the builders, so the biosynthesis of proteins, polysaccharides, nucleic acids and other organic compounds depends on components (a), (b) and (c) above. Let us consider these further and see how far they take us towards some biochemical questions posed later in this Section.

2.1 THE BLUEPRINT

As you know, the plan or blueprint is DNA in all animals, plants, fungi, prokaryotes and also in many viruses. You have learned in earlier Units that DNA contains information coded within a sequence of nucleotides and that this information defines the form of the organism. Environment also plays its part but, given enough cat food, oxygen and water, cat DNA leads inevitably to cats. Equally, given enough space, light, oxygen, minerals, carbon dioxide and water, oak tree DNA leads inexorably to oak trees. Within any particular species of organism, the same kind of relationship applies. For example, the DNA of different alleles of maize determines different grain characteristics—either purple or white, or smooth or wrinkled. How does DNA influence the biochemical events in cells that somehow give rise to these phenotypic differences?

5

PRECURSOR

METABOLISM

It is essential to an appreciation of biochemistry to understand the reality of these relationships. Everything about an organism is influenced by the biochemical processes within it: a rubber tree makes rubber because its cells possess the right kind of reactions, a black moth is black because its biochemical pathways make quantities of the dark pigment melanin, someone with sickle-cell anaemia has the condition because there is a defect in their haemoglobin. All these examples involve the DNA of genes giving overall direction to the biochemistry of the cell. The question is, how?

Section 2.3 of Unit 19 dealt briefly with the link between the DNA plan and biochemical reality: 'DNA makes RNA makes protein' is the phrase which expresses that link most succinctly. Though the details of the route from DNA to protein must be left to Unit 24, the crucial point for now is the idea that different genes bring about the formation of different proteins and that these different proteins are the 'machine tools' of the cells, bringing about different kinds of biochemical reaction, hence different phenotypes.

You met an example of this relationship between gene, protein and phenotype in Unit 21:

☐ What is the effect of the Hb^S allele compared with the Hb^A allele?

■ An abnormal protein, haemoglobin S, is produced instead of the normal protein, haemoglobin A. This has several phenotypic effects, as discussed in Unit 21, Section 3.3.

Later, you will discover that almost every biochemical reaction in the cells of every organism depends on the involvement of very specific proteins. As there are thousands of different reactions, there are thousands of different proteins, each one made by its own specific gene and bringing about some tiny part of biochemistry. Many of these proteins are enzymes (you met these briefly in the discussion of catalysis in Unit 16 and again in Units 17–18), and others that are not enzymes (haemoglobin for example) have nonetheless essential roles.

You will hear much more about enzymes and other proteins in later Sections. For now, the point to remember is that growth from zygote to adult is achieved through biochemical processes mediated by proteins that are, in turn, determined by genes. This relationship is summarized in Figure 2.

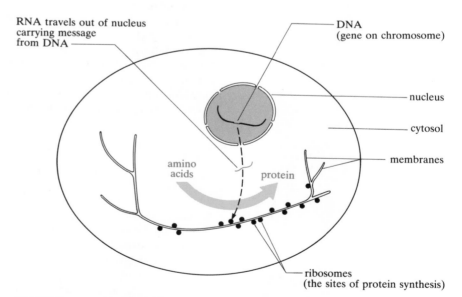

RNA travels out of nucleus carrying message from DNA

DNA (gene on chromosome)

nucleus

cytosol

membranes

amino acids

protein

ribosomes (the sites of protein synthesis)

FIGURE 2 DNA makes RNA makes protein. Proteins determine the nature of cell biochemistry.

2.2 THE ORIGIN OF CELLULAR SUBSTANCES

To return to the house-building analogy introduced earlier, what are the 'bricks and mortar' of which cellular chemicals are made? And, moreover, where do organisms get them from? Let us start with the biochemical events within cells and defer for a while the question of the source.

You already know some of those principal cellular chemicals. In particular, the important biopolymers—proteins, nucleic acids (DNA and RNA) and polysaccharides such as starch—have all been mentioned. Another group of substances that are not polymers, but that nevertheless have an important role in all cells, are the fats. In all cases the question is: From what smaller molecules are these cellular substances made? In other words, what are the **precursors** of proteins, nucleic acids and so on?

☐ Using your knowledge from Units 17–18, what are the likely precursors of proteins and of DNA?

■ In cells proteins are synthesized from amino acids and DNA is synthesized from nucleotides.

You will see shortly that the precursors of polysaccharides are simple sugars called monosaccharides, and fats are formed from simpler substances called fatty acids and glycerol. The chemistry of all these cellular substances and the details of the routes by which they are synthesized are not important at this stage; the crucial point is that the complicated set of biochemical reactions inside each cell, termed the **metabolism** of the cell, generates all the necessary precursors from which are built the material of the cell itself. Figure 3 summarizes these relationships.

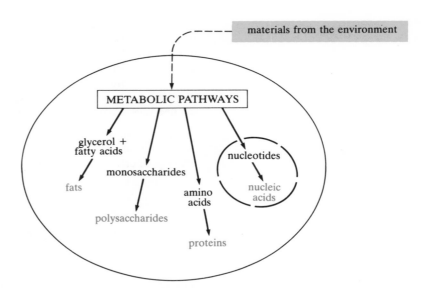

FIGURE 3   Precursors, produced from materials taken in from the cell's environment, are converted to a variety of cellular chemicals. The biochemical reactions involved are part of the metabolism of the cell.

Figure 3 also shows that materials from the environment enter cells and form the precursor molecules—our next problem is to consider the nature of these materials. A human zygote has a mass of a microgram or less, whereas an adult human may be around 70 kg. The great increase is, clearly, a result of taking in materials from outside. The same kind of increase is encapsulated in the phrase 'tall oaks from little acorns grow'. Here, inside the acorn, an embryo of less than a gram grows to become a tree of many tonnes. So, in both animals and plants, the question is: *What* substances are taken in from the environment?

AUTOTROPH

HETEROTROPH

ASSIMILATION

PHOTOSYNTHESIS

ANABOLISM

MUSCULAR WORK

BIOLUMINESCENCE

CONCENTRATION GRADIENT

ACTIVE GRADIENT

To answer this we need to recognize the very important division of living organisms into two groups which have different modes of nutrition. These are the autotrophs and the heterotrophs. *Auto* is the Greek for self and *troph* means feed. Similarly, *hetero* means other. Green plants are 'self-feeders' so are **autotrophs**, while animals feed on 'other things' so are **heterotrophs**. The definition of these fundamentally different modes of nutrition is based on the source of the element carbon. An autotroph obtains its carbon solely from atmospheric or dissolved carbon dioxide. In contrast, a heterotroph obtains the carbon of its cellular compounds by taking in ready-made organic molecules from the environment. This is called **assimilation**. When a heterotroph assimilates organic molecules, it takes them across a membrane into its interior. For example, an animal assimilates organic molecules when it absorbs digested food in its intestine.

☐ Look at the classification of organisms on the back cover of this book. Which other groups besides animals do you think are heterotrophs?

■ Fungi and some species of bacteria. Fungi secrete enzymes that hydrolyse the organic material on which they grow, and assimilate the small soluble molecules produced. Many bacteria live on organic matter. *Escherichia coli*, the bacterial species that you have met several times before, lives in the 'organic soup' of the large intestine.

Although the definitions of autotrophs and heterotrophs are based on carbon, most heterotrophs also obtain their supplies of nitrogen and of sulphur in organic form. These elements are essential: nitrogen is present in proteins and nucleic acids and sulphur is a constituent of several naturally occurring amino acids. And, as we shall see shortly, heterotrophs obtain the energy they need by breaking down (usually by oxidation) the organic compounds they assimilate.

Consideration of the heterotrophs leads us inevitably to think about autotrophs. This is because the latter are the source of ready-made organic molecules that heterotrophs assimilate, either directly for herbivores (plant eaters) or indirectly for carnivores (flesh eaters). This relationship is one of the fundamentals of ecology and is reviewed extensively in Unit 25. It is important to note here the link between ideas of ecology and the biochemical needs of animal and plant cells.

What further should be said of autotrophs? You know from the discussion above that all green plants use carbon dioxide as their carbon source. What other properties do they share?

ITQ 1   Reflect on what you know from general knowledge about the way plants live and, in horticultural and gardening terms, are cared for. What is the primary source of energy in plants? From what sources do plants obtain the elements nitrogen and sulphur?

The answer to this question has highlighted the process of **photosynthesis**. This is the process by which most autotrophs (that is, all green plants and most autotrophic bacteria) use light energy to bring about the synthesis of organic cellular molecules from carbon dioxide and water, with the concomitant production of oxygen. Clearly, at this point, our discussion of the source of cellular material is merging into a consideration of the source of energy. Before moving on to consider this in the next Section, look at Figure 4 which summarizes the main points about the sources of the elements carbon, hydrogen, nitrogen and sulphur in autotrophs and heterotrophs.

2.3 ENERGY

Of equal and fundamental importance to the provision of raw materials is the question of the supply and utilization of energy in organisms. What, in energetic terms, is going on in the animals and plants whose growth and survival is of so much interest to us? Questions about energy occur time

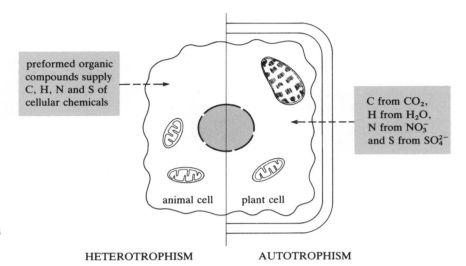

FIGURE 4 Sources of some of the main elements from which cell chemicals are made in autotrophs and heterotrophs.

HETEROTROPHISM   AUTOTROPHISM

and again in most of the following biology Units, and it is worthwhile taking the discussion in three steps: processes that require energy, processes that make energy available and the link between the two.

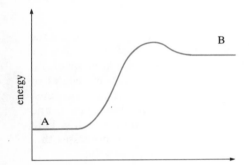

FIGURE 5 Profile of the chemical energy change for a reaction of the type: A (precursors) ———→B (large molecule). (This is related to the enthalpy reaction profile you met in Unit 16.)

Energy-requiring processes

Making large molecules from smaller precursors is one energy-requiring process that has already been introduced. The chemical energy change associated with a biosynthesis of the type

$$\text{A (precursors)} \longrightarrow \text{B (large molecule)}$$

is usually of the general form shown in Figure 5. Clearly, to *add* chemical energy to a system will require its supply from somewhere else—you met these ideas of energy conservation in Unit 9.

Providing energy for biosynthesis, or **anabolism** as it is also called, is not the only energy transformation that occurs in organisms. Cast your mind back to some of the energy conversions that were discussed in Unit 9. Then, reflecting on your general knowledge of the life of both animals and plants, try ITQ 2.

ITQ 2 Think of a growing tree, a crawling baby, and a glow worm. Think of their internal processes as well as their obvious activities. What processes or activities involve the expenditure of energy?

Let us have a closer look at some of the items listed in the answer to ITQ 2. The idea of an organism increasing its own gravitational energy or kinetic energy (or that of some object such as a cricket ball) is a familiar one. In animals, such changes are brought about by **muscular work**.

A few organisms—fire-flies and glow worms are obvious examples—convert some of the energy available to them into light, and so exhibit what is termed **bioluminescence**.

Much more widespread (in fact it occurs in all organisms) is the use of energy to move molecules or ions from a place where their concentration is low to a different place where their concentration is high—that is, *against* a **concentration gradient**. A real example of this situation is shown in Figure 6 (overleaf): to move nitrate ions from the soil (where their concentration is usually low) into the cytosol of the cells that form the root hairs (where nitrate ion concentration is usually higher) requires energy—rather like pumping water up a hill. Therefore, movement of this kind is termed **active transport**. There are many other examples of active transport throughout biology: making urine in the kidneys, facilitating the entry of many different kinds of substances into cells and even generating electrical impulses in nerves, all involve movement of ions or molecules against a concentration gradient, and so require the expenditure of energy.

9

CATABOLISM

AEROBIC RESPIRATION

ADENOSINE TRIPHOSPHATE (ATP)

ADENOSINE DIPHOSPHATE (ADP)

INORGANIC PHOSPHATE (P_i)

ENERGY TRANSDUCER

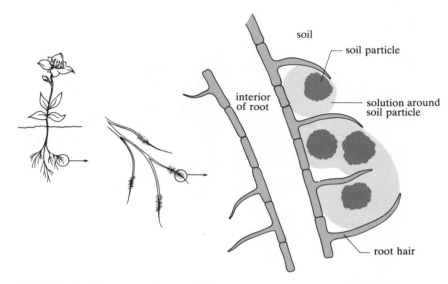

FIGURE 6   Movement of nitrate ions into the cytosol of root cells by active transport. The relative intensity of the pink tone denotes the relative concentration of nitrate ions.

anabolism + catabolism

= metabolism

catabolism releases energy

anabolism uses (stores!) energy

The one item in the answer to ITQ 2 that has not so far been discussed is heat. You know from Unit 9 that many energy conversions lead to the appearance of energy in the form of heat: the impact of a ball on the ground or of the flow of an electric current along a wire are familiar examples. So it is in living systems, also. When muscles contract, molecules or ions are transported, or chemicals are synthesized, there is an associated production of heat. This heat production has important biochemical and physiological consequences which you will meet in Section 4 of this Unit and again in Unit 23. For now, however, we shall turn from processes that require the expenditure of energy to the question of energy supply.

The supply of energy

As stated in Unit 9, energy cannot be created or destroyed. So, whatever quantities of energy are expended in the various processes discussed above, the same quantities must be supplied from some source outside the organism.

☐ What is the external source of energy in heterotrophs?

■ Organic compounds (such as glucose) assimilated from the environment. These are then broken down by various chemical reactions in such a way that the chemical energy of those compounds becomes available for use in the energy-requiring processes.

These 'breaking down' types of reactions are properly termed catabolic reactions and, together, make up that part of metabolism called **catabolism**. (Anabolism and catabolism together constitute metabolism.) As you will see later, many catabolic processes involve *oxidizing* organic compounds to carbon dioxide and water. Thus most respiration in animals and plants depends on oxygen, and is termed **aerobic respiration**.

Turning now to autotrophs, the environmental source of energy for almost all of these is the Sun. Solar radiation (red and blue light in particular) is absorbed by green plants and by green prokaryotes, and is used to bring about the synthesis of carbohydrate from the carbon dioxide and water taken in from the environment. Once formed within the cell or cells of the autotroph, the fate of the newly synthesized organic material is almost identical to that of assimilated molecules in heterotrophs. The molecules are catabolized, usually through oxidation, and as a consequence yield up energy that thus becomes available to the energy-requiring processes of the plant—biosynthesis and active transport.

So in autotrophs and heterotrophs chemical energy is made available for a variety of energy-requiring processes, by catabolism. But what kinds of energy conversion are involved in the transmission of energy within cells?

Energy transmission within organisms

How is the chemical energy of coal converted to the kinetic energy of the wheels of a steam engine? Or, the chemical energy of petrol to the kinetic energy of a speeding car? You will have little difficulty in identifying the first step: the fuel is burnt and heat is released. In all such 'heat engines'—for that is the general class of energy converters to which cars and steam engines belong—the heat generated is caused to flow from a very hot place (the furnace or combustion chamber) to a much cooler place, ultimately the outside environment. As the heat flows, it does work, via the expansion of gases, that converts part of the heat energy to kinetic energy.

The intriguing feature of energy transmission in organisms is that it does not and *cannot* occur in this way. General knowledge tells you that high temperatures cannot be tolerated by living tissue. (You will learn why in Section 4.) In fact, although some heat is generated as a by-product, energy is passed from the energy-yielding catabolic reactions to the energy-requiring processes by an entirely different method that depends crucially upon the interconversion of two substances, **adenosine triphosphate (ATP** for short) and **adenosine diphosphate (ADP)**.

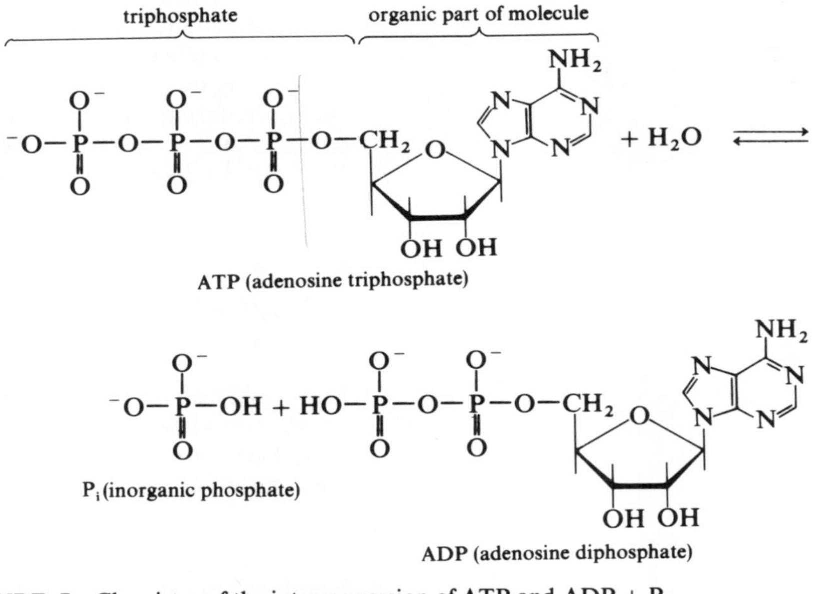

FIGURE 7   Chemistry of the interconversion of ATP and ADP + P_i.

ATP has a relative molecular mass of around 500, and is found in every cell of every species that has been examined. As Figure 7 shows, the ATP molecule contains three connected phosphate groups (*tri*phosphate) attached to an organic part. One of these can readily be removed by hydrolysis to give ADP and an **inorganic phosphate** ion, written in conventionally abbreviated form as P_i. The structure of ADP contains the same organic part and, of course, just *two* connected phosphates. The interconversion is often written simply as:

$$\text{ATP} \rightleftharpoons \text{ADP} + P_i$$

You need to know this abbreviated form of the ATP/ADP interconversion, but *not the full structural formulae*.

The role of ATP, as noted earlier, is to take chemical energy made available by catabolic reactions to the various processes that require energy. As such ATP is often described as an **energy transducer**—the term meaning, literally, a 'leader across of energy'. In a simple and inexact model, you can consider

ATP as a 'wound-up chemical clockwork motor' and ADP as the 'run-down chemical clockwork motor', working as shown in Figure 8. The catabolic processes on the left wind the motor up, and the wound-up motor drives the energy-requiring processes on the right. As a consequence of that, the motor runs down and is ready for rewinding by further catabolic activity. You can appreciate this energy-carrying capacity if you note that the synthesis of one mole of ATP from ADP and P_i requires about 30 kJ and, conversely, the conversion of one mole of ATP makes the same amount of energy available to energy-requiring systems. The production of heat at the points at which ATP is formed and used is shown in Figure 8 and will be referred to again in later Sections.

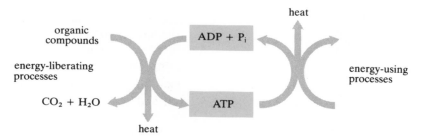

FIGURE 8   The role of ATP, ADP and P_i in energy transduction.

In conclusion, a word of caution about pictorial analogies such as that developed above: they are almost always inaccurate. Of course ATP is not a molecule with a spring and it doesn't wind up and unwind; nor does energy dart out from the glucose oxidation and in some miraculous way cause the synthesis of ATP from ADP and P_i. Equally, on the right-hand side of Figure 8, energy from ATP does not just flow across into the energy-requiring systems. How ATP is made and how it is used is a complex and sometimes contentious field. The key point, however, is that the ADP/ATP system links catabolism and the energy-using processes.

2.4 BIOCHEMISTRY AND THE SURVIVAL OF ORGANISMS

Section 2.3 has, we hope, given you a good idea of what kinds of biochemical activity underlie growing and surviving. It is important but sometimes quite hard to relate a very chemical subject (increasingly so in the rest of this Unit) to more accessible whole-organism biology.

If you have ever owned a kitten and watched it grow to maturity then on into middle age, you will have been aware of feeding, excretion, movement, breathing and perhaps reproduction. With the more chemical perspective introduced above, you might now be asking: How, precisely, is the carbohydrate, protein and fat of its diet oxidized within its cells to make ATP from ADP and P_i? As you watch the kitten grow, you might also wonder: How is the ATP and the material of its food used to make new cat cells? Still other biochemical questions could well occur to you: How does the cat's metabolism go faster when it runs and go slower when it sleeps? How does the colour of a cat's fur relate to the cat's biochemistry and so to its genotype?

If, in addition to your cat, you have some favourite house plant carefully grown from a seed, you may now be wondering about its biochemistry as an autotroph. You will reflect that the water and fertilizers applied to its roots, and the carbon dioxide in the air of your living room (a concentration of barely 0.04%), together with the light energy entering through the window, give the literally thousands of different compounds of which the plant is made. And you now know that at night—when there is no photosynthesis, but the plant remains healthy—the plant (like an animal) respires its food stores to drive its metabolic processes. You also know that in the day both photosynthesis *and* respiration occur at the same time.

To add substance to that biochemical framework, to examine in detail the role of enzymes in metabolism, and to study the mechanism and sites of ATP production, we shall have to look much more closely at what goes on inside cells. We begin with a look at the nature of cellular chemicals and at the structure and function of enzymes.

SUMMARY OF SECTION 2

1 Growth, in the sense of making new cell chemicals, occurs in all organisms. Growth and survival are essential if organisms are to live to reproduce.

2 Growth requires a blueprint (DNA), materials (precursor molecules and the environmental substances that give rise to precursors), and biologically useful energy in the form of ATP.

3 DNA fulfills its role as blueprint by directing the synthesis of specific proteins that in turn have specific metabolic roles.

4 Precursor molecules are formed during metabolism from (ultimately) raw materials taken into the organism from the environment. These are assimilated organic compounds in the case of heterotrophs, and carbon dioxide, water and various inorganic ions in the case of autotrophs.

5 In heterotrophs, energy is provided by catabolism of organic compounds obtained in the diet. Much catabolism is oxidative and CO_2 is produced.

6 In most autotrophs energy is provided by light. The organic compounds formed by photosynthesis are catabolized much as in heterotrophs.

7 Energy-requiring processes include biosynthesis (anabolism), active transport, muscular work, and bioluminescence. Heat is produced as a by-product.

8 The link between energy-producing and energy-using reactions is provided by the interconversion of ATP and ADP + P_i.

SAQ 1 If you put a geranium plant in a sealed glass box in bright sunlight for an hour, and measured the oxygen and carbon dioxide concentration at the beginning and end of that period, what changes would you expect and why?

SAQ 2 If you repeated the experiment in SAQ 1 but, this time, kept the box in a dark cupboard, what gas changes would you expect and why?

SAQ 3 A particular strain of the bacterial species E. coli is able to live (generation after generation) suspended in a solution which contains dissolved glucose as the only source of carbon. What kinds of other substances must also be dissolved in the solution if it is to grow successfully?

SAQ 4 The E. coli cells (of SAQ 3) obtain energy by oxidizing the glucose in the solution. What changes in gas content would you expect in the air above the solution?

SAQ 5 Suppose you used glucose labelled with carbon isotope ^{14}C in the E. coli suspension. In what kinds of compounds inside the E. coli cells would you expect to find ^{14}C after several hours?

SAQ 6 A different strain of E. coli is able to live (generation after generation) in a solution which contains a different kind of sugar called fructose. It is not able to make use of glucose. The difference between the two strains of E. coli is a genetic one. How do you think these differences in nutrition could arise from their genetic differences?

SAQ 7 When you run, what change (if any) will occur in: (a) the amount of ATP in your muscles; (b) the carbon dioxide output from your lungs; and (c) your heat output?

METABOLIC PATHWAY

METABOLITE

INTERMEDIATE

PYRUVIC ACID

FAT

FATTY ACID

STEARIC ACID

PALMITIC ACID

GLYCEROL

3 THE CHEMICAL CONSTITUTION OF ORGANISMS

Most parts of most organisms are composed mainly of water, in humans about 80%. And although there are exceptions (such as spores, pollen and seeds) you can think of the cells of organisms as bags of dissolved substances containing membranes and organelles made of insoluble molecules. We need to enquire about these soluble and insoluble compounds, for without some knowledge of them catabolism and anabolism would remain a mystery.

Most of these are organic substances, but others—also of great biological importance—are inorganic. Insoluble inorganic compounds include the complex calcium phosphates (also fluorides) of bones and teeth, the calcium carbonate of shells, and the silicon dioxide of the hard cap at the tip of plant roots. In addition, there are dissolved anions such as nitrate, chloride, sulphate, phosphate, carbonate and bicarbonate; and cations such as sodium, potassium, magnesium and calcium. These inorganic ions have many different roles: the part the bicarbonate ion plays in transporting carbon dioxide in blood is discussed in Unit 23, sodium and potassium ions have key roles in the conduction of nerve impulses and phosphate, of course, has an essential job in energy transduction. Nitrate and sulphate ions, as you already know, are the major sources of nitrogen and sulphur for autotrophs.

But it is on the world of organic molecules that most details of metabolic processes depend and, after dealing briefly with small organic molecules, we consider fats, polysaccharides and then proteins.

3.1 SMALL ORGANIC MOLECULES

The term 'small' is usually applied to molecules with a relative molecular mass of up to a few hundred: there is, however, no hard and fast dividing line between large and small molecules. There are very many different compounds within the category, including the precursor molecules you met earlier and various other compounds involved in cell biochemistry.

You were introduced to the idea of metabolism in the last Section and, as you will increasingly discover, metabolism is the whole set of biochemical reactions that occur inside cells. This set is composed of a large number of interlinking **metabolic pathways**. The molecules involved in these sequential reactions are called **metabolites** or metabolic **intermediates**. A given pathway will have, of course, a precise number of different reactions of a particular kind. Each one of these reactions will be catalysed by its own specific enzyme.

☐ What is the significance of the fact that each reaction in a metabolic pathway is catalysed by a specific enzyme?

■ From the discussion in the previous Section, it is through the production of particular enzymes that DNA influences what kind of biochemistry will occur.

Thus, we can write a kind of generalized metabolic pathway using letters to represent the sequence of different metabolites: A ⟶ B ⟶ C ⟶ D ⟶ E and so on. Each metabolite has its own name, formula and role. Although you will explore several pathways in some detail later, you need to know the identities and names of very few metabolites indeed. One that you must know, however, is **pyruvic acid**, pronounced 'pie-roov-ic' acid. (You will appreciate its key role in metabolism later.) Table 1 gives the name, formula and role of some important metabolites, including precursor molecules mentioned earlier.

TABLE 1   Some important metabolites and their roles in metabolism

Name and type of compound	Formula	Role in metabolism
pyruvic acid	$CH_3-\overset{\displaystyle \|}{\underset{\displaystyle O}{C}}-\overset{\displaystyle \|}{\underset{\displaystyle O}{C}}-OH$	intermediate in the catabolism of glucose
alanine (an amino acid)	$CH_3-\underset{\displaystyle NH_2}{\overset{\displaystyle \|}{CH}}-\overset{\displaystyle \|}{\underset{\displaystyle O}{C}}-OH$	amino acids such as alanine are the precursors of proteins
glucose (a monosaccharide)	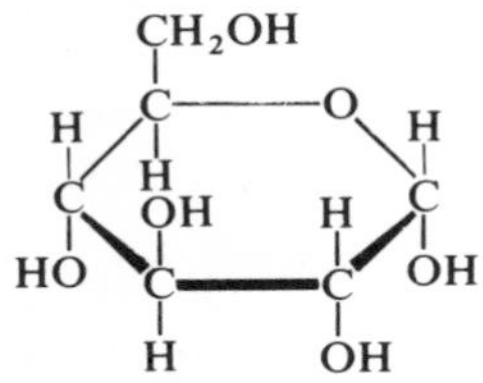	the precursor of polysaccharides (e.g. starch, cellulose glycogen)
glycerol (an alcohol)	CH_2-OH $\|$ $CH-OH$ $\|$ CH_2-OH	involved in the structure of fats
palmitic acid (a fatty acid)	$CH_3-(CH_2)_{14}-\overset{\displaystyle \|}{\underset{\displaystyle O}{C}}-OH$	fats are esters of glycerol and fatty acids
stearic acid (a fatty acid)	$CH_3-(CH_2)_{16}-\overset{\displaystyle \|}{\underset{\displaystyle O}{C}}-OH$	

SAQ 8   Cells X, Y and Z, are concerned, respectively, with the biosynthesis and storage of haemoglobin, fat and glycogen. Which of the small molecules (i)–(vi) below will be intermediates in each kind of biosynthesis?

Z (i) glucose   (iv) deoxyribose
X (ii) alanine   (v) pyruvic acid
  (iii) glycerol   Y (vi) palmitic acid

wrong! see answer (handwritten)

3.2 FATS

What are **fats**? Everyone is familar enough with this group of chemicals—lard, suet, butter, corn oil and olive oil are everyday kitchen examples. All of these originate from animals and plants which gives a hint of how widespread and important these compounds are in living things. The structure of fats is fairly simple: they are esters of long-chain carboxylic acids, usually called **fatty acids** (such as **stearic acid** and **palmitic acid**) and an alcohol called **glycerol***—the latter containing three hydroxyl groups per molecule (see Table 1). You met esters in Units 17–18 (Section 5.3) where you saw that an ester is formed when a carboxylic acid condenses with an alcohol. The example you met then was:

$$CH_3-CH_2-OH + CH_3-\overset{\displaystyle \|}{\underset{\displaystyle O}{C}}-OH \rightleftharpoons CH_3-CH_2-O-\overset{\displaystyle \|}{\underset{\displaystyle O}{C}}-CH_3 + H_2O$$

ethanol   acetic acid   ethyl acetate
(alcohol)   (carboxylic acid)   (ester)

As indicated in the above equation, the reaction is reversible—ethyl acetate

---

* Glycerol is also called glycerine. You may have this colourless sweet liquid in your kitchen.

LIPASE

TRIGLYCERIDE

PHOSPHOLIPID

MONOSACCHARIDE

GLUCOSE

SUGAR

CARBOHYDRATE

CELLULOSE

AMYLOSE

AMYLOPECTIN

GLYCOGEN

is hydrolysed to ethanol and acetic acid. Hydrolysis of fats into glycerol and fatty acids can be catalysed by an enzyme called **lipase**. (You met this enzyme in Units 17–18, Section 5.3.) Though ethyl acetate is an ester it certainly is not a fat! In fats, as noted above, the alcohol is always glycerol. Also, the carboxylic acid molecules (there are *three* in each fat molecule because there are three hydroxyl groups to condense with) are not acetic acid molecules but compounds of the same type much further up the homologous series.

☐ Do you recall from Units 17–18 what distinguishes one member of a homologous series from the next?

■ Adjacent members differ by a —CH_2— group. You should be able to see (from Table 1) that palmitic acid and stearic acid are members of the same carboxylic acid (fatty acid) series and differ in chain length by two —CH_2— groups.

So fats are esters of *glycerol* and *three* molecules of one or more kinds of long-chain fatty acids; not surprisingly, they are also called **triglycerides**.

ITQ 3   Given that the formation of an ester between a molecule of glycerol and three palmitic acid molecules is analogous to the formation of ethyl acetate from ethanol and acetic acid, write a balanced equation for the reversible reaction involved in the formation of the fat, glyceryl tripalmitate.

Triglycerides (simple fats) are not the only kind of fatty substance: **phospholipids**, so-called because they contain phosphate groups, are involved in the structure of all membranes in all cells. The simple fats described above are used as food stores in animals and plants. In animals, these fat stores also provide heat insulation and shock absorbancy. You know at least some of this from general knowledge and everyday observations: the cushioning layer of fat around animal kidneys and hearts that you see in the butcher's shop protect those organs from shock; and the thick fatty layer under the skin of a pig is a good illustration of thermal insulation. The oil (a liquid form of fat) that serves as a food store in maize grains, sunflower seeds and olives is used by humans in large quantities for cooking.

As a group, fats illustrate a feature that we shall come across with increasing frequency and significance in both Sections 3 and 4 of this Unit, and again in Unit 24. This feature is the close relationship between the structure of molecules and their biological function—to be expected if evolution has been effective! One of the chief roles of fat is as a food store. Many compounds used in food storage are insoluble—starch and fats are examples that you know from everyday experience. Why, in molecular terms, are fats so insoluble? Their relative insolubility in the highly polar solvent water is exactly what you would expect for molecules containing long chains of —CH_2— groups such as palmitic acid and stearic acid. You studied this kind of relationship in Section 3.2 of Units 17–18.

You will meet fats again later in this Unit when we consider how fats are catabolized inside cells to yield ATP. This is the ultimate fate of the fat we eat.

SAQ 9   When incubated at 30 °C with the enzyme lipase, the pH of an emulsion of fat droplets gradually falls. Explain this. (Hint: Remember that carboxylic acids are ionized in aqueous solution.)

SAQ 10   Write out the structural formula of the fat produced in the reaction between one molecule of glycerol, two molecules of stearic acid and one molecule of palmitic acid. Is there another possible structure you could have drawn?

3.3 POLYSACCHARIDES

You met this class of biopolymer in Units 17–18, learning there that polysaccharides, nucleic acids and proteins are all condensation polymers—big molecules formed when many monomers join by the elimination of water molecules.

☐ What will happen if you hydrolyse any of these polymers?

■ The constituent monomers are re-formed.

The name polysaccharide says quite a lot about structure: *poly* means many, so polysaccharide means many saccharides; or, more correctly, many **monosaccharides**. The latter are simple sugars, such as **glucose**, that cannot be hydrolysed into any smaller molecule.

If you liken one monosaccharide molecule to a bead capable of being joined to another, it is easy to picture a molecule of two beads, three beads and so on. These are called *di*saccharides, *tri*saccharides etc. If you add enough (thousands usually, but the number, even in a given type of molecule, is imprecise), you get a polysaccharide. Polysaccharides are usually relatively or very insoluble and are not sweet. On the other hand, monosaccharides (such as glucose and fructose), disaccharides (such as sucrose or table sugar) and trisaccharides are soluble and sweet: collectively they are **sugars**. Another related term is **carbohydrate**. This is a collective term encompassing polysaccharides *and* sugars.

Polysaccharides are present in the cells of all organisms and have many biological roles. Table 2 lists some examples. Note, in passing, how important polysaccharides are to many areas of human activity—paper and timber production, and the manufacture of starchy foods such as bread, cakes and biscuits, are obvious examples. Other uses may be surprising: alginic acid is important to the seaweeds from which it comes, but instant desserts and other manufactured foods depend on it too!

TABLE 2   Some naturally occurring polysaccharides

Name	Type	Occurrence	Role
cellulose	homopolymer of glucose, unbranched	plants	the main structural component of plant cell walls
amylose	homopolymer of glucose, unbranched	plants	food store: a component of starch
amylopectin	homopolymer of glucose, branched	plants	food store: a component of starch
glycogen	homopolymer of glucose, branched	animals	food store, mainly in muscles and liver
chitin	unbranched non-glucose homopolymer	crustaceans and insects	forms horny exoskeleton
chondroitin sulphate	complex heteropolymer	animals	structural component of cartilage
alginic acid	unbranched non-glucose homopolymer	seaweeds	structural component of cell walls in seaweeds

Of the compounds listed in Table 2, only four are discussed further in this or the following Units. These are (in plants) **cellulose**, **amylose** and **amylopectin**, and (in animals) **glycogen**. Table 2 summarizes their functions and you should take particular note of these. Unlike some of the more complex polysaccharides in the Table, the tough fibres of cellulose and the rather insoluble food-storage substances of amylose, amylopectin and glycogen are all polymers of the monosaccharide glucose. But, if these are all homopolymers of glucose, how can their properties be so different? You can get a good way towards an answer using 'chemical common sense'.

☐ How is it possible to construct different overall structures with only one kind of monosaccharide?

■ By having sequences of different length and by having branched or unbranched structures.

A third way in which polysaccharide structures can differ from each other is in the stereochemistry of the link between the constituent monosaccharides. In Figure 9 you can see that D-glucose (the biologically occurring optical isomer) exists in two configurations: the α form and the β form. The difference lies in the direction of the C^1—OH bond: it points downwards in the α form and upwards in the β form in this diagram. Within organisms, dis-

FIGURE 9   (a) The full structures of α-D-glucose and β-D-glucose. Note that the two forms are interconvertible and differ in the configuration of the hydroxyl group on C-1. The plane of the ring is indicated by the wedge-shaped bonds; the hydrogen atoms and hydroxyl groups lie above and below this plane. (b) Simplified structures of α-D-glucose and β-D-glucose. Notice that neither the ring carbon atoms nor the hydrogen atoms to which they are attached are shown. This is the convention used for carbohydrate structures from hereon in the text.

solved glucose is an equilibrium mixture of the two forms, but in polysaccharides the configuration of the C^1—O bond is fixed and determines the nature of the link between the constituent **glucose residues**. Figure 10 shows the structures of the four polysaccharides amylose, amylopectin, glycogen and cellulose, and serves to illustrate these points.

If this all sounds a matter of somewhat abstract chemistry, think again! As shown in Figure 10, a linear sequence of glucose residues in the α configuration is amylose—a major nutritional component of human diet. In contrast, a linear sequence of glucose residues in the β configuration is cellulose, and this polysaccharide is of no nutritional use at all in the human diet. So, abandoned in a jungle, whether you starved or not could depend on the direction of the C^1—O bond!

Not surprisingly, herbivores—directly or through their gut bacteria—*are* able to utilize cellulose. This nutritional difference arises because of the properties of two different hydrolytic enzymes: **amylase** is able to hydrolyse bonds between α-glucose residues, whereas **cellulase** is able to hydrolyse only those bonds occurring between β-glucose residues. The hydrolysis of these two kinds of **glycosidic bond** is shown in Figure 11.

There are, as you can see from Figure 10, other differences between the molecules besides bond type. Amylose and cellulose are linear molecules (many thousands of glucose residues in length), whereas glycogen and amylopectin are both highly branched molecules (and usually contain even more residues per polymer molecule). The nature of the branch points is easily appreciated if you recall that the glucose molecule has several hydroxyl groups: if you imagine a chain of residues joined by α-1,4 glycosidic bonds, you can picture a branch chain (also α-1,4 linked within itself) being 'grafted on', so to speak, via an α-1,6 glycosidic bond (see Figure 10).

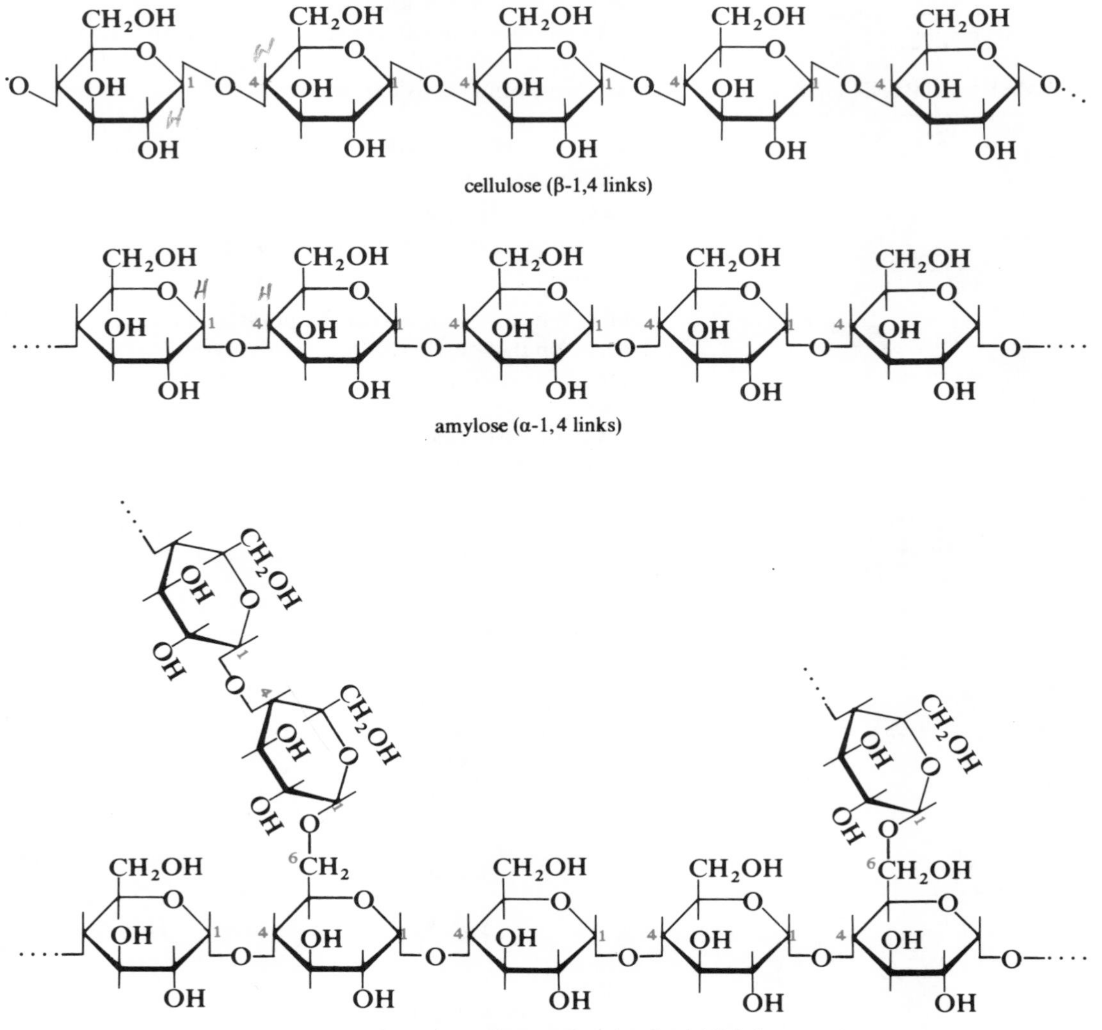

cellulose (β-1,4 links)

amylose (α-1,4 links)

amylopectin or glycogen (α-1,4 *and* α-1,6 links)

FIGURE 10   The structures of cellulose amylose, amylopectin and glycogen. The glucose residues are joined by α-1,4 links in amylose, amylopectin and glycogen, but by β-1,4 links in cellulose. Branching of the chains occurs in both amylopectin and glycogen via α-1,6 links.

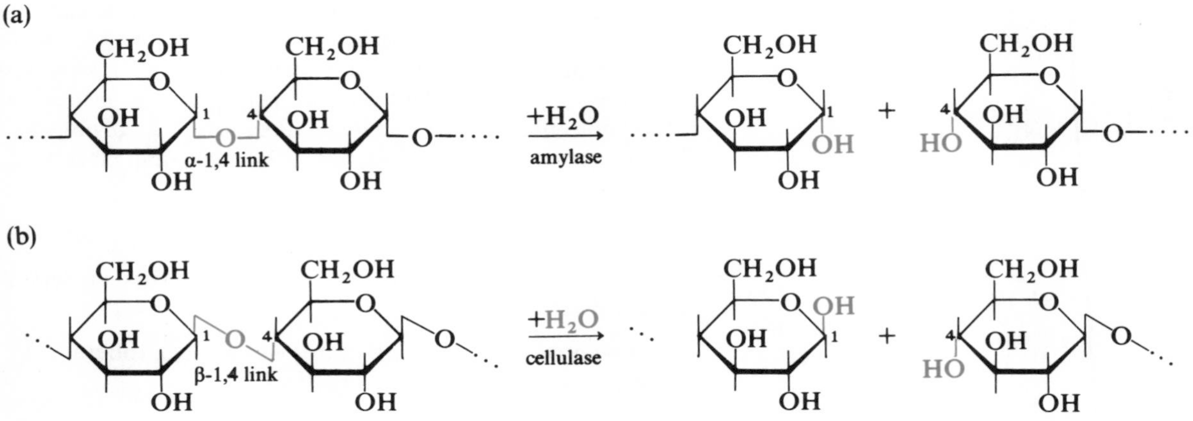

(a)

(b)

FIGURE 11   The hydrolysis of glycosidic bonds. (a) Amylose hydrolysis by amylase; (b) cellulose hydrolysis by cellulase. The enzymes hydrolyse many such bonds in each polysaccharide molecule.

PROTEIN

R GROUP

N-TERMINAL RESIDUE

C-TERMINAL RESIDUE

POLYPEPTIDE

PRIMARY STRUCTURE

4 bonds ∴ 4×H₂O.

Cellulose

Cellulos β1-4 links Cellulase

A   Isomaltos

B   Maltose

C - Cellobiose

To conclude our brief discussion of this essential group of cellular chemicals, you should note that the molecular structure of polysaccharides—hence their physical and chemical properties—accord very much with their biological role. For example, the shape conferred on the cellulose molecule by the directionality of the β-1,4 glycosidic bonds permits the formation of a strong, fibrous structure. This is very much what is required of plant cell walls, where evolutionary adaptation at the molecular level will have selected wall molecules that are both strong and flexible. This kind of molecular structure/biological function relationship will become yet more apparent as we move on to consider proteins.

SAQ 11   How many water molecules are formed when a pentasaccharide is formed from its constituent monosaccharides?

SAQ 12   The digestive system of a snail contains a hydrolytic enzyme that permits it to digest the principal polysaccharide constituent of plant cell walls.

(a)   What is the name of the polysaccharide that is hydrolysed?
(b)   What type of bonds are hydrolysed?
(c)   What is the name of the enzyme?

SAQ 13   Maltose and cellobiose are disaccharides produced by the partial hydrolysis of amylose and cellulose, respectively. Maltose and isomaltose are the two disaccharides that are produced by the partial hydrolysis of glycogen. From your knowledge of the structure of each of these polysaccharides, match the formulae A, B and C to the three named disaccharides.

This question is quite hard and may be omitted.

Yeah! I did it!

3.4 PROTEINS

The importance of **proteins** hardly needs emphasizing further. Whether as *enzymes* (catalysts), *transport proteins* (such as haemoglobin), *contractile proteins* (such as those in muscles), *immunoproteins* (in the body's defence system), *membrane proteins* (in the structure of cells), *structural proteins* (as in tendons or hair) or *hormone proteins* (such as insulin), each different protein molecule is made under the direction of its own gene, and performs its own precise biological function. The task that faces us here is to discover:

What are the common structural features of all proteins?

What is it that makes the structure of one protein different from another?

How do the differing structures endow each different protein molecule with unique biological properties?

Common structural features

The idea of a condensation polymer is by now a fairly familiar one, and, as you know, proteins, like polysaccharides and nucleic acids, belong to this category. Each protein molecule is a condensation heteropolymer of amino acids. As it is a *hetero*polymer, it is composed of more than one kind of amino acid residue.

In fact, about 20 different kinds of amino acid are involved in the structure of most kinds of protein molecule. You met glycine, alanine, phenylalanine and serine in Units 17–18 and, for reasons that become clear later, you need to be aware of the names and formulae of four more: these are aspartic acid, glutamic acid, lysine and cysteine. Table 3 lists the formulae of these eight—and, for interest, the names of the other 12. The conventional abbreviations of all 20 amino acids are also shown. You do not need to remember names or formulae, but should be able to follow a discussion involving them.

TABLE 3 Some of the amino acids found in proteins. The naturally occurring amino acids have the general formula $R-\underset{\underset{NH_2}{|}}{CH}-\underset{\underset{O}{\|}}{C}-OH$

Amino acid	Abbreviated name	R group (shown in ionized form where appropriate)
glycine	Gly	$H-$
alanine	Ala	CH_3-
phenylalanine	Phe	$Ph-CH_2-$
serine	Ser	$HO-CH_2-$
aspartic acid	Asp	$\overset{-}{O}-\underset{\underset{O}{\|}}{C}-CH_2-$
glutamic acid	Glu	$\overset{-}{O}-\underset{\underset{O}{\|}}{C}-(CH_2)_2-$
lysine	Lys	$\overset{+}{N}H_3-(CH_2)_4-$
cysteine	Cys	$HS-CH_2-$

The other amino acids are valine (Val), leucine (Leu), isoleucine (Ile), threonine (Thr), methionine (Met), tyrosine (Tyr), tryptophan (Trp), arginine (Arg), asparagine (Asn), glutamine (Gln), histidine (His) and proline (Pro).

At the top of the Table you can see the general formula for amino acids: note that the **R group** of each kind of amino acid is different. The formation of a *tripeptide* (three amino acid residues joined together) can be represented as shown below. Notice that the carboxyl group of one amino acid condenses with the amino group of the next. At one end (on the left in the conventional representation) there is a free amino group and at the other, there is a free carboxyl group. These end amino acid residues are known as the **N-terminal residue** and **C-terminal residue**, respectively.

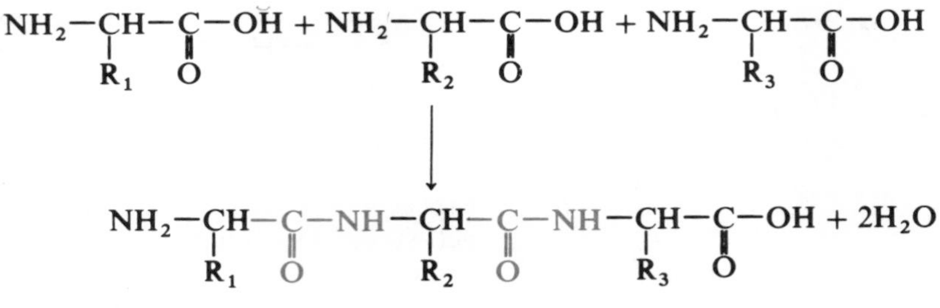

$$NH_2-\underset{\underset{R_1}{|}}{CH}-\underset{\underset{O}{\|}}{C}-OH + NH_2-\underset{\underset{R_2}{|}}{CH}-\underset{\underset{O}{\|}}{C}-OH + NH_2-\underset{\underset{R_3}{|}}{CH}-\underset{\underset{O}{\|}}{C}-OH$$

$$\downarrow$$

$$NH_2-\underset{\underset{R_1}{|}}{CH}-\underset{\underset{O}{\|}}{C}-NH-\underset{\underset{R_2}{|}}{CH}-\underset{\underset{O}{\|}}{C}-NH-\underset{\underset{R_3}{|}}{CH}-\underset{\underset{O}{\|}}{C}-OH + 2H_2O$$

As you can see, there is a repeated sequence of atoms, $-\underset{\underset{O}{\|}}{C}-NH$ (shown in red), in this equation. It occurs between each amino acid residue and is termed a peptide bond (Units 17–18). From this simple equation, you should be able to picture the formation of a **polypeptide** by the condensation of *many* amino acid molecules to give a long chain of amino acid residues connected to each other by peptide bonds. Such a structure, involving nothing but covalent bonds, is termed the **primary structure** of the protein. This is shown in Figure 12 (overleaf).

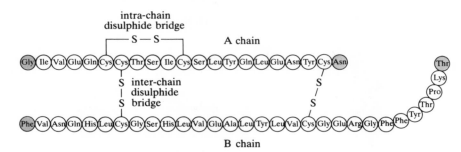

$$NH_2-CH-C-NH-CH-C\cdots\cdots-NH-CH-C-NH-CH-C-OH$$

FIGURE 12   The primary structure of proteins. The parts shown in pink boxes at either end are the (left) N-terminal and (right) C-terminal amino acid residues. (The line of dots indicates that part of the sequence has been omitted.)

Structural differences between proteins

With so many different proteins doing so many different things, it is clear that there must be an enormous variety of structure. How can this be, given that they are all polymers of (at most) 20 different monomers? Asked this way, the question is easily answered. Because there are 20 different kinds of amino acid molecule and because a protein chain can contain up to several hundred amino acid residues, there exists a huge number of possible *sequences*. In fact, there are 20^{25} (about 3.4×10^{32}) different ways a polypeptide of only 25 residues long can be constructed from 20 different amino acids! As some protein molecules contain two hundred or so residues, you can see that the molecular structure of protein gives plenty of scope for effectively endless variety. Every different protein in your body is unique because it has its own unique sequence of amino acid residues in its primary structure. Figure 13 shows the primary structure of the hormone **insulin**.

FIGURE 13   The primary structure of human insulin. The protein has two polypeptide chains, A and B, with 21 and 30 amino acid residues, respectively. The A and B chains are held together by disulphide bridges, formed between cysteine residues. The C-terminal residues are shown in pink and the N-terminal residues in grey.

This is a noteworthy example, as insulin is discussed extensively in Units 23 and 24. Note that in the insulin molecule, two polypeptide chains are held together by **disulphide bridges**. These are formed from the —SH groups of two cysteine residues:

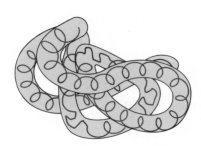

$$\cdots\cdots-SH + HS-\cdots\cdots \xrightarrow{\text{oxidation}} \cdots\cdots-S-S-\cdots\cdots$$

—SH groups of cysteine residues   disulphide bridge

When proteins are made in cells (look back at Figure 2), it is the long 'necklace-like' primary structure that is first made. But, as various kinds of experiment have shown, this newly-formed molecule has no biological activity at all until, in ways discussed later, the primary structure of a protein gathers itself up into a three-dimensional globular structure (left). The precise shape of each globular structure, called **higher-order structure**, is unique to each protein and confers on it its unique biological properties.

There are three questions we should address:

(a)   How does a gene determine primary structure?
(b)   How does primary structure determine higher-order structure?
(c)   How does higher-order structure determine biological function?

This sequence of questions is summarized in Figure 14.

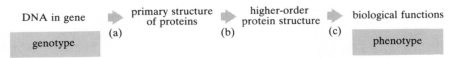

FIGURE 14 (a) How does the gene determine primary structure? (b) How does primary structure determine higher-order structure? (c) How does higher-order structure determine biological function?

Primary structure, higher-order structure and biological function

Look again at Figure 14. The route labelled (a) will be left until Unit 24. For now, just note that somehow DNA directs the condensation of amino acids in a particular sequence. What of route (b)? How does a particular sequence of amino acids give rise to a particular globular shape? The answer is because **weak bonds** (that is, non-covalent bonds) occur between amino acid residues in different but highly specified parts of the linear chain. Imagine a metre tape-measure stretched out. Suppose you now fix a piece of rubber band between the 10 and 80 cm marks and between the 95 and 50 cm marks and then lay the tape measure out on a table. You might well get a crumpled strip that looks something like the illustration on the left.

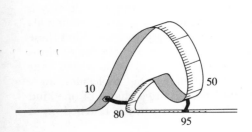

Weak bonds acting on a chain of amino acid residues give a more precise response than our mechanical analogy and an exact and highly specific higher-order structure always results. Some of those weak bonds are the hydrogen bonds you met in Units 17–18. These cause parts of the 'necklace' to coil up into a helical shape rather like the cable of a modern telephone hand-set. Thus our sequence of beads becomes a fattish sausage, as illustrated on the left.

Among other significant types of weak bond are the rather precise **ionic interactions** between the various R groups of the amino acid residues along the chain. For example the negatively charged R group of aspartic acid (Table 3) might be attracted to the positively charged R group of lysine. The kind of 'rubber band' effect is like this:

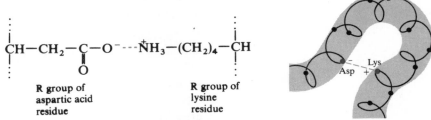

What you can now appreciate is that the location of these weak electrostatic bonds will depend crucially on which R groups are in which positions along the sequence of amino acid residues. Thus, higher-order structure will arise spontaneously as a consequence of the sequence of amino acid residues (the primary structure). And, moreover, a mutation which leads to an alteration in amino acid sequence could have a devastatingly large effect on higher-order structure, hence biological properties. The Hb^S allele is one such mutation—the replacement of a negatively charged glutamic acid residue (in HbA) by an electrically neutral valine residue (in HbS) has a large structural effect and, as you know, a large effect on phenotype.

We are left with route (c) of Figure 14: the relationship of higher-order structure to biological function. Proteins that are biochemically active—either as enzymes or, like haemoglobin, with some other function—have a broadly globular shape.* In fact, they are collectively termed globular proteins (Units 17–18). Experimentally, it is also clear that a globular protein exerts its biological effect by binding reversibly with the substance on which

---

* Most *structural* proteins (for example, the protein keratin of which hair is made) are in the form of long fibres, and are termed fibrous proteins (Units 17–18). These are not discussed further here.

it is acting. For example, an enzyme binds with the reactants of the reaction it catalyses, haemoglobin binds with oxygen, and so on. This kind of reversible binding, essential for activity, occurs at particular sites on the precisely shaped surface of the globular protein. If a change in primary structure gives a change in higher-order structure with the result that the binding site is deformed in some way, then the biological activity of the protein will be diminished or even destroyed.

Some idea of the precise shape associated with higher-order structure may be gained from Plate 1, which is a schematic diagram of a molecule of the protein **myoglobin**; and from Plate 2, which shows a schematic model of a **haemoglobin** molecule.

Myoglobin is similar to haemoglobin, though its molecular mass is only a quarter that of haemoglobin. It is found in the muscles of diving mammals such as whales and seals, and has an oxygen-carrying power such that these mammals can remain under water for 80 minutes or more. Haemoglobin is a much larger molecule, composed of four polypeptide chains and four **haem** groups. In simple terms, it is like four myoglobin molecules stuck together. Note that each haemoglobin molecule has two chains of one kind (α chains) and two of another kind (β chains). This point is touched on in Unit 24.

None of these details should be memorized or even worried over. The key point is that biochemically active proteins have precise globular shapes, with sites that bind other substances. This, as you will see in the following Section, is of the utmost significance for enzyme function.

SUMMARY OF SECTION 3

1 Small organic molecules are the metabolites of cells; some of these are precursors in the biosynthesis of cellular components.

2 Fats are esters of glycerol and long-chain fatty acids. They have various roles, for example in food storage.

3 The class of compounds called carbohydrates comprises polysaccharides and sugars. Sugars include monosaccharides, disaccharides etc. Polysaccharides are condensation polymers of monosaccharides.

4 Some polysaccharides are complex heteropolymers. Those studied in this Section are all homopolymers of glucose. Differences in their structure arise from differences in chain length, whether the chain is branched or not and differences in the stereochemistry of the glycosidic bonds.

5 Polysaccharides perform many roles, notably structural ones (for example, cellulose in plants) and food storage ones (for example, glycogen in animals and amylose and amylopectin in plants). Molecular structure is related to biological function.

6 Proteins are condensation heteropolymers of 20 different kinds of amino acids. The amino acid residues are linked by peptide bonds. Proteins have very diverse roles; for example, as enzymes and transport molecules.

7 Every different protein has a different sequence of amino acids, called its primary structure. Primary structure determines higher-order structure (via weak bonds, especially ionic interactions). Higher-order structure determines binding sites, and hence the biological activity of the protein.

8 Genes determine metabolic activity by directing the formation of proteins of unique primary structures.

9 Insulin, myoglobin and haemoglobin provide good examples of many of the characteristic properties of globular proteins.

SAQ 14   Which of the following statements are true?

(a) All proteins yield amino acids when they are hydrolysed.   *YES.*
(b) A molecule of any protein contains all 20 kinds of amino acids.   *No*
(c) A polypeptide containing 100 amino acid residues has 100 peptide bonds.   *99*
(d) A mutation leading to a change in just one amino acid residue in a polypeptide always has an effect on higher-order structure.   *NO.*

SAQ 15   What kind of molecule would result if the N-terminal amino group of a polypeptide condensed with the C-terminal carboxyl group of the same molecule?

SAQ 16   Why is it correct to say that all proteins are polypeptides but not all polypeptides are proteins? (Hint: Compare the structures of haemoglobin, insulin and myoglobin.)

4   THE ROLE OF ENZYMES IN METABOLISM

As noted in Section 2.1, there are several thousand different **enzymes** in a cell. Many are in solution in the cytosol and in the fluids within the organelles. Others are insoluble and are bound in the membranes of cells—molecular islands of globular proteins set in a sea of phospholipid molecules. Some enzymes are secreted by cells into the solution outside the cells, for example, the enzymes of the digestive system. Most, however, do their essential work within cells, assisting the movement of molecules and ions across membranes and catalysing the myriad reactions of cell metabolism.

If you were playing some biochemical party game and had to respond to the challenge 'Enzymes?' in not more than three words, those words would probably be *catalyst*, *specific*, and *protein*. Almost every reaction in all organisms is catalysed by a particular enzyme; that is, the rate of reaction A $\longrightarrow$ B is increased by the effect of the enzyme A-ase. If that enzyme were isolated and its catalytic power investigated *in vitro* (literally 'in glass'; that is, in a test-tube or other laboratory apparatus, rather than in the whole cell or organism), you would find that it would catalyse only that reaction, or one very similar to it; that is what **enzyme specificity** means. And finally, analysis of the isolated enzyme would show it to be a protein, sometimes with a non-protein attachment called a **prosthetic group*** (so named because, like an artificial limb or *prosthesis*, the group is fixed on to the protein molecule).

Each different enzyme is a different globular protein, made, of course, at the direction of its own particular gene. The specific shape of the globular molecule permits it to bind particular **substrates**, another name for the reactants in an enzyme-catalysed reaction. And it is this binding that permits catalysis and confers specificity.

Note that the names of most enzymes end in '-ase' and begin with a word or part-word that describes either one of the substrates of the enzyme or the kind of reaction it catalyses. Let us now look further into these very varied, life-sustaining molecules.

---

* Some non-enzyme proteins also have a prosthetic group; for example, haem is the prosthetic group of haemoglobin.

4.1 ENZYME CATALYSIS

One of the most characteristic features of organisms is that reactions occur inside them at relatively rapid rates, and this is due to **enzyme catalysis**. A bag of sugar will sit on a shelf, unoxidized by the oxygen of the air around it, for years. Yet taken into solution inside the person who eats the sugar, the reaction $C_6H_{12}O_6 + 6O_2 \longrightarrow 6H_2O + 6CO_2$ occurs as soon as glucose reaches the cells. A mixture of nitrogen and hydrogen will hardly react at all at room temperature on their own. Yet, nitrogen-fixing bacteria inside the root nodules of plants such as beans or clover produce ammonia at a rate sufficient to supply both the bacteria and the host plant. In doing this, the bacterial enzyme **nitrogenase** catalyses the reaction $N_2 + 3H_2 \longrightarrow 2NH_3$ with an effectiveness that far exceeds the activated iron catalyst of the Haber–Bosch process! (Unit 16, Section 7).

From these examples, it is clear that cells possess very powerful catalysts. A striking quantitative example is provided by the enzyme **carbonic anhydrase** which is found in red blood cells. This important enzyme catalyses the reaction that occurs when carbon dioxide dissolves in water. You will meet this enzyme again in Unit 23. The reaction catalysed is:

$$CO_2 + H_2O \rightleftharpoons H^+ + HCO_3^-$$
$$\text{bicarbonate ion}$$

Without the enzyme, the reaction is very slow: with the enzyme, however, the rate is *ten million times* as great.

So, it is clear that enzymes permit reactions to occur at the kind of rates necessary for life. You know from Unit 16 that they do not alter the equilibrium position of a reaction but they do, like all catalysts, lower the activation energy of the reaction. Figure 15 shows this.

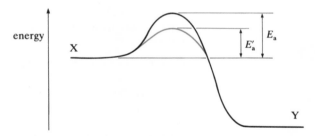

FIGURE 15   Curve showing the energy changes associated with the reaction X $\longrightarrow$ Y. E_a is the activation energy in the uncatalysed reaction, and E_a' is the much lower activation energy of the enzyme-catalysed reaction.

How does an enzyme lower activation energy? To ask this is to ask about the mechanism of enzyme action, and a detailed answer would differ for every different enzyme. But a crucial feature common to all is that the enzyme molecule binds with the substrate to form what is called an **enzyme–substrate complex**. As a consequence of this binding, bonds within the substrate are distorted, activation energy is lowered, and catalysis occurs. The product or products (for example, ammonia in the nitrogenase example) are then released from the enzyme surface, and the enzyme molecule is then free to bind again with more substrate and to continue catalysis. The process is summed up in the general equation:

$$\underset{\text{enzyme}}{E} + \underset{\text{substrate}}{S} \rightleftharpoons \underset{\substack{\text{enzyme–substrate} \\ \text{complex}}}{ES} \longrightarrow \underset{\text{enzyme}}{E} + \underset{\text{product}}{P}$$

Substrate molecules are bound at a special site on the surface of the globular enzyme molecule termed the **active site**. As you can appreciate from your knowledge of the higher-order structure of proteins, the active site will have a very precise shape and contain a particular set of amino acid residues—contributed, perhaps, by quite different parts of the polypeptide chain. Figure 16 shows how a substrate can bind to the active site to give

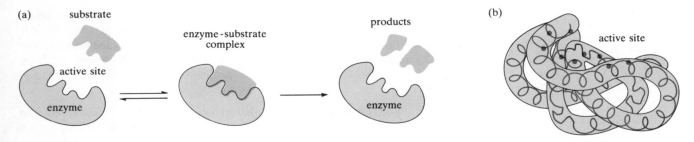

FIGURE 16 (a) The lock and key model of enzyme action. The grey-shaded shape representing the structure of the enzyme is shown in more detail in (b). Here you can see that the higher-order structure of the enzyme molecule gives rise to the active site. The amino acid residues at the active site (shown as red spots) contribute to the catalytic power of the enzyme by binding to and straining bonds within the substrate molecule.

the enzyme–substrate complex that breaks down to give enzyme and product. Complex experimental methods of investigating molecular structure show that this so-called **lock and key model** of enzyme action is broadly true for most enzymes.

4.2 ENZYME SPECIFICITY AND ITS IMPORTANCE IN METABOLISM

If the shape and chemical nature of a substrate molecule have to match the shape and chemical nature of the active site in this kind of 'lock and key' way, we have an excellent explanation of enzyme specificity. An enzyme will, as noted earlier, catalyse only one reaction or, sometimes, one *kind* of reaction. The fat-hydrolysing enzyme lipase is a good example of the latter type.

Enzyme specificity is of the utmost importance in the organization and control of metabolism. A metabolic pathway or route is a sequence of reactions, occurring in cells, by which some substantial biochemical transformation is brought about. As you already know, if the route involves breaking a molecule into smaller molecules it is a catabolic route, and if it involves making a larger molecule it is an anabolic route. The catabolism of glucose (to carbon dioxide and water) is an example of the former and illustrates an important general point. The *overall* process of glucose breakdown is exactly the same as that occurring when glucose powder burns in a flame. However, *in vivo* (inside the living cell or organism), the reaction is spread over about 30 different reactions, each one catalysed by its own enzyme. As you will see shortly, adjustments to the activity of these highly specific, glucose-catabolizing enzymes provide cells with a means of regulating the rate of catabolism to match the respiratory needs of the organism.

Glucose catabolism is just one of many metabolic routes, all of which interconnect in the overall biochemistry of the cell. The organization of the flow of substrates through these pathways depends on enzyme specificity, and the particular route followed at any time through these interconnecting pathways depends on the relative activities of those enzymes at that time. Consider Figure 17, which shows a hypothetical set of linked pathways A, B and C. The black dots denote metabolic intermediates, and the red arrows the enzymes that are most active. Thus in Figure 17a route B predominates and in Figure 17b route C is the predominant pathway. If analogies help your thinking, you may like to picture metabolism as a sort of

FIGURE 17 Organization of metabolism by the relative activities of different specific enzymes. In (a) the enzymes of route B are most active, while in (b) route C enzymes are most active.

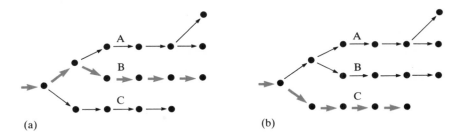

'biochemical London Underground', with different metabolic routes being the interconnected lines. The changing activities of different enzymes will alter the flow of metabolites along them, with the 'District Line' busy at one time and the 'Circle Line' busy at another. Once again, which lines are busy at any particular time will depend on the needs of the organism.

ITQ 4 You know about the higher-order structure of proteins and you know about enzyme active sites. Describe briefly how the activity of an enzyme might be made to vary in the ways implied above.

4.3 THE EFFECTS OF TEMPERATURE AND pH

Variations in temperature or pH greatly affect enzyme activity. This matters very much to organisms. If either changes by too much, death is the inevitable result. What is the nature of these effects and how can they be explained?

Suppose you want to investigate the effect of temperature on the initial rate of the reaction X $\longrightarrow$ Y, catalysed by the enzyme X-ase. What you would do is to set up a series of tubes containing the substrate X in solution, put the tubes into water baths at different temperatures, add a set amount of X-ase and start a stop-watch. After (say) a minute you would stop* the reaction and measure the amount of Y formed (or the amount of X used). From this you could work out the 'moles of X converted to Y per minute' in the first minute of the reaction, at each temperature used. If you then plotted initial rate—often termed **enzyme activity**—against temperature, your plot would look something like that in Figure 18a.

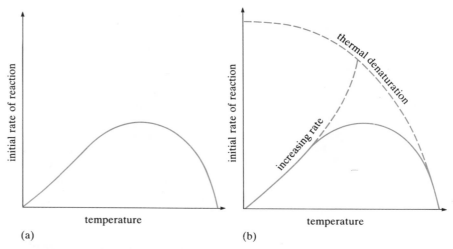

FIGURE 18   (a) A plot of the initial rate of an enzyme-catalysed reaction against the temperature of the solution in which the reaction occurs. (b) The two underlying (and opposing) processes that give rise to the curve in (a).

All enzymes give the kind of plot shown in Figure 18a. As temperature increases, activity goes up, levels off, then falls ever more sharply until it reaches zero. The question is: Why are enzyme activity against temperature curves this shape? The left-hand part of the plot is what you might have expected from your study of reaction rates in Unit 16. You saw there that most reactions go faster at higher temperatures, so it seems entirely reasonable that the rate of the reaction A $\longrightarrow$ B should be increased. However, as this is a *catalysed* reaction, the rate will also depend on the presence of an effective catalyst. Enzymes are proteins and it happens that the higher-order structure of proteins is progressively destroyed as tem-

---

* How you stop an enzymic reaction is discussed at the end of Section 4.3.

perature increases. This temperature-related destruction of proteins is called **thermal denaturation**. (On an extreme scale, it is the same as what happens when you boil an egg, when the protein of egg-white is denatured and becomes insoluble.)

The rate-increasing effect and enzyme-destroying effect of increasing temperature thus oppose each other. Figure 18b shows how these opposing effects give rise to the activity against temperature curve in Figure 18a.

☐ From your knowledge of higher-order structure, why do you think that proteins become progressively more denatured as temperature increases?

■ Because higher-order structure depends entirely on weak bonds (such as ionic interactions). As temperature increases and the kinetic energy of the protein molecule increases, those bonds are broken.

☐ From your knowledge of the mechanism of enzyme action, why do you think these changes in higher-order structure decrease activity?

■ Because the active site of the enzyme molecules is progressively destroyed.

Even if it may seem so from Figure 18, enzymes do not have a true optimum temperature—for where the curve peaks depends both on how the experiment is conducted and on the organism from which the enzyme has been isolated. Most often activity is greatest between about 35 and 45 °C. But there are some marked exceptions in some species. For example, the Antarctic icefish, with a body temperature of around −2 °C, has a satisfactorily active metabolism. At the other extreme, the thermophilic ('heat-loving') bacteria which live in pools of volcanic water boiling at 105 °C clearly contain proteins which are highly resistant to heat denaturation. Both instances are probable examples of evolutionary adaptation at a molecular level, and the enzymes in each case may well have an optimum far outside the 35–45 °C range.

The upward sloping and downward sloping parts of Figure 18 have major physiological consequences for organisms. For example, if human temperature is reduced from the normal 37 °C to 27 °C, the metabolic rate falls some 40%. This is put to use in medical practice; for example, organs removed for transplantation are packed in ice to reduce metabolic rate and so preserve them until re-use. Conversely, if body temperature stays at 43 °C (109 °F), cell proteins become damaged so that death eventually ensues. In organisms that normally maintain a nearly constant body temperature, such as birds and mammals, even quite small changes in internal temperature lead to biochemical and physiological disturbances in most species. On the other hand, animals that do *not* regulate their internal temperature by metabolic means (reptiles, for example) are much more active at high temperatures than at low ones. Aspects of the physiology of temperature regulation are discussed in Unit 23.

Let us leave now the question of temperature, and turn to the effect of pH. As you will remember from Unit 15, this is a gauge of the concentration of dissolved hydrogen ions—an acid solution has a high concentration of H^+ ions and therefore a low pH. Organisms are extremely sensitive to their internal pH, and in humans, as in other species, a range of physiological systems operate to maintain pH within a narrow range. In a healthy adult, the pH of plasma (the non-cellular part of blood) in arteries is usually in the range 7.40 ± 0.05 (though the cells of different tissues have other 'standard' values). If plasma pH moves outside the range 7.0–7.8, death is likely. Why is this?

ITQ 5 As you know, the activity of an enzyme depends on the active site on each molecule. From what you know of the higher-order structure of proteins, write a sentence or so explaining how variations in pH could affect the activity of an enzyme. (Hint: Recall from Unit 15 how the degree of ionization of weak acids varies with pH).

pH OPTIMUM

PEPSIN

COENZYME

DEHYDROGENATION

ALCOHOL DEHYDROGENASE

NAD

FAD

As you see from the answer to ITQ 5, those amino acids that have ionizable R groups—aspartic acid, glutamic acid and lysine are examples from Table 3—are very important in maintaining higher-order structure. A change in pH will markedly alter the ionization of those groups and, therefore, the charge that they bear. Because of this, the nature of the weak bonds within the protein structure changes, and the shape of the protein molecule and its active site are also likely to vary. If this happens, the ability of the active site to bind the substrate and catalyse the reaction will also alter. Figure 19 illustrates the kind of pH-induced change that can occur.

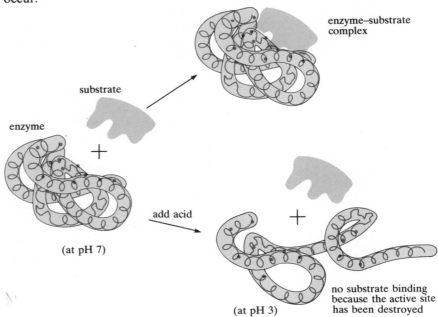

FIGURE 19   Changes in pH can have a marked effect on the active site, and hence biological activity. In the Figure, the amino acid residues at the active site are denoted by red spots. (The effect shown is exaggerated.)

Thus it is not surprising there is a particular pH at which a given enzyme is most active. This is known as its **pH optimum**. At other pH values, the activity will be lower, and at extreme pH values, the enzyme protein may become irreversibly denatured. A plot of enzyme activity against pH, typically a bell-shaped curve, is shown in Figure 20. Such a curve is obtained experimentally by measuring the activity of a particular enzyme at a whole series of different pH values. Each enzyme plus substrate reaction, in a solution of a particular pH, gives a particular point on the curve.

Different enzymes have different pH optima. For example, **pepsin**, a digestive enzyme that hydrolyses proteins in our very acid stomachs, has a pH optimum of about 2. In contrast, the enzymes of some bacteria growing in alkaline soda lakes in East Africa have pH optima around 11.

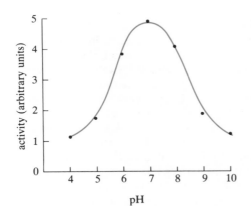

FIGURE 20   Typical bell-shaped curve showing how the initial rate of an enzyme-catalysed action varies with pH. The enzyme in this case has a pH optimum of 7.

At the conclusion of this discussion of the effects of temperature and pH, you are now in a position to understand how it is possible to 'stop' an enzyme-catalysed reaction very rapidly. On page 28, you read that the reaction catalysed by X-ase was 'stopped after one minute'. Experimentally that could have been done either by putting each test-tube into a bath of boiling water or by adding strong acid. Either treatment so disrupts the active site that all catalytic activity is abolished.

4.4 COENZYMES

Coenzymes are small organic molecules that 'work with' enzymes (hence the name), and are a sort of 'ancillary substrate' in biochemical reactions. They are not proteins and do not, by themselves, catalyse reactions.

Many enzymic reactions involve the **dehydrogenation** of a substrate, that is, the removal of (usually two) hydrogen atoms from the substrate molecule. You will come across many examples of dehydrogenation later in this Unit, but an immediate example is the conversion of ethanol to acetaldehyde:

$$CH_3-CH_2-OH + X \longrightarrow CH_3-CH=O + XH_2$$

ethanol   acetaldehyde

The reaction, catalysed by the enzyme **alcohol dehydrogenase**, occurs in the liver, and is most important in detoxifying our systems after drinking ethanol (whisky is a 40% solution of this alcohol!). You can see that two hydrogen atoms are transferred from ethanol to some hydrogen-carrying molecule which is thereby reduced: X is reduced to XH_2. X is an example of a hydrogen-carrying coenzyme (or group transfer molecule, as coenzymes are sometimes known). Effectively it is a second substrate, but it is special in that it is present in very small amounts. The implication of this point is that, for the reaction to continue, XH_2 must be reconverted to X very rapidly. The characteristics of low cellular concentration and rapid recycling are what distinguish a coenzyme from an ordinary substrate. As you will discover later, the particular identity of X is **NAD** (short for nicotinamide adenine dinucleotide). Thus the equation above should be written as:

$$CH_3-CH_2-OH + NAD \longrightarrow CH_3-CH=O + NADH_2$$

It is interesting to note that the number of different enzymes in an organism far exceeds a thousand, yet the number of different coenzymes hardly reaches ten! In fact, to be precise about the number would depend on how some substances are classified. The important point is that there are not very many, and one kind of coenzyme serves many different enzymes. You will meet five different ones in this Unit and these are listed in Table 4.

You must know these names!

TABLE 4   Some coenzymes

Exam question (difference?)

Abbreviation	Name	Metabolic role
NAD	nicotinamide adenine dinucleotide	carries hydrogen atoms as $NADH_2$
NADP	nicotinamide adenine dinucleotide phosphate	carries hydrogen atoms as $NADPH_2$
FAD	flavin adenine dinucleotide	carries hydrogen atoms as $FADH_2$
Q	coenzyme Q	carries hydrogen atoms as QH_2
CoA	coenzyme A	activator of fatty acids

Though the full names can be safely forgotten, the initials or other abbreviated names by which they are conventionally known are important. Some of these will become quite familiar through constant usage; in particular NAD and **FAD** (flavin adenine dinucleotide) will be old acquaintances by the end of Section 6.

Most coenzymes have a relative molecular mass of around a few hundred. Their formulae are relatively complicated—as are many of the chemical reactions in which they do their group transfer jobs. One feature common to most is of particular significance. Their structures contain within them organic components that certain species are unable to synthesize for themselves.

☐ NAD is present in very small quantities in cells but is essential for their biochemical well-being. A component of NAD is the substance niacin. Niacin cannot be made in the body. What can you conclude?

■ Small quantities of niacin must be assimilated. Thus niacin is, in small quantities, an essential dietary component.

31

VITAMIN

ENZYME ASSAY

ACHROMATIC TIME

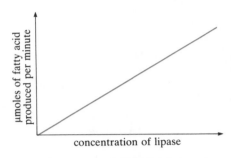

FIGURE 21   A plot of initial rate of reaction (μmoles of fatty acid produced per minute under defined conditions) against concentration of lipase.

An organic substance, such as niacin, that is needed in small quantities in the diet is called a **vitamin**. Niacin is also a component of NADP; and riboflavin, also a vitamin for humans, is part of the structure of FAD. Vitamins that are involved in coenzyme structure are collectively termed B group vitamins.

4.5 MEASURING THE CONCENTRATION OF ENZYMES IN SOLUTION

Suppose you were to do an experiment to see how the initial rate of a reaction varies with different concentrations of enzyme. Provided there is excess substrate and the pH and temperature are constant in all measurements, the result would be the simple relationship: *rate is proportional to enzyme concentration*. Figure 21 shows the result of such an experiment for the enzyme lipase. This clear-cut linear relationship is noteworthy for two reasons:

1   It is consistent with the lock and key model of enzyme action (discussed in Section 4.1).
2   It provides biochemists with a way of measuring the concentration of enzymes in solution.

Regarding the first point, this experimental relationship is exactly what you expect if the model were true. If substrate concentration is at all times in excess, the active sites on the enzyme molecules will be saturated with substrate. Thus, the more molecules of enzyme that there are present, the greater the concentration of the enzyme–substrate complex and the greater the rate of product formation. If an analogy helps, consider this. If you have a thousand football fans (i.e. plenty of substrate) and supply *one* bus to transport them to the match, you will achieve a certain, rather miserable, rate! (The bus is the enzyme and the fans-at-the-match is the product.) If you supply *two* buses (twice the amount of enzyme), you will achieve twice the rate. If three buses, three times the rate, and so on. Clearly if there were only half a dozen fans, more buses don't help: substrate must be saturating.

Regarding the second point, the linear relationship between rate and enzyme concentration is of very great applied significance, especially in the world of health care. Clearly, by measuring the rate of a particular enzyme-catalysed reaction under standard conditions, it would be possible to compare the concentrations of that enzyme in different solutions. (For example, twice the concentration would give twice the rate.) By doing this on various body fluids, blood plasma in particular, substantial amounts of diagnostic information about various illnesses are made available. **Enzyme assay**, the measurement of enzyme concentration, is a major part of the work of every hospital biochemistry laboratory.

Because blood circulates through every tissue and organ in the body, plasma contains small quantities of many cellular enzymes. If a malfunction occurs in some part of the body, such as the heart, liver or prostate gland, there is often a surge in the plasma level of a particular enzyme, indicative of the particular malfunction in the particular organ. Some interpretations are relatively straightforward: alcohol dehydrogenase is present mainly in the liver, and an increase in the plasma level of this enzyme indicates a liver problem. Other diagnoses based on assay of plasma enzymes are more difficult, especially where organs do not have particular 'typifying' enzymes. However, by reference to the pattern of release of *several* enzymes, information about the function of most organs can be obtained.

4.6 PROPERTIES OF SALIVARY AMYLASE

You were asked in the Study Guide to make sure you had some arrowroot. You were also asked to make a solution of it. (The instructions are given on p. 34.) If you have not already made your arrowroot solution, do so now: the hot solution needs to cool to room temperature before you use it.

One of the main aims of this experiment is to let you see an enzyme working. The source of the enzyme you will use, amylase, is your own saliva. The substrate it acts on is amylose: this kind of starch is a major constituent of arrowroot. The reaction catalysed is:

$$\text{amylose} + \text{water} \longrightarrow \text{dextrins}$$

Look back at Figure 10 to see the structure of amylose. Dextrins are sequences of glucose residues condensed together, much longer than sugars but much shorter than amylose. If the reaction is allowed to continue further, the dextrins are further hydrolysed to trisaccharides and, eventually, to disaccharides as well.

What you are asked to do in the experiment described overleaf is to set up a rather unsophisticated assay system. As noted above, the principal aim is simply to see the enzyme working: however, if the experiment goes well for you, you may obtain an index (called the achromatic time) that will enable you to compare the concentration of amylase in your saliva with that of others you meet at your Study Centre.

☐ From your knowledge of enzyme assay, how might the rate of this enzyme-catalysed reaction be measured?

■ By measuring *either* the rate of disappearance of amylose *or* the rate of formation of the dextrins (or sugars).

In the experiment, you will use the first of these alternatives. The gauge of amylase concentration is simply the time it takes for detectable amylose to disappear from the reaction mixture: this is the **achromatic time** (literally 'no colour time'). Residual amylose is detected by the formation of a very deep blue, rather grainy solution when iodine solution is added. If all amylose molecules have been hydrolysed as far as dextrins, you would see a slightly grainy reddish brown coloration. And if only sugars remain, you would see only the 'tea-without-milk' colour of the iodine solution. Look at Plate 3 to get an idea of these colours.

There are difficulties associated with this experiment. The most awkward is that some people do not have any amylase in their saliva—and do not know it until they try the experiment! (There is evidence that smoking reduces salivary amylase activity.) So you may get a negative result. If this is the case, you should NOT *do the experiment with someone else's saliva*. Official health guidance is that **experiments using body fluids should be done only with fluids provided by the experimenter in person**.

Another more superficial difficulty is almost the converse. Some people have so much amylase that the reaction is very fast—so fast that it is hard to believe it has happened.

As regards manipulation, there are two important points. When dissolving your starch, the water must be boiling. Secondly, all your glassware must be scrupulously clean because amylase is readily inactivated by contaminants. The iodine solution also inhibits the reaction, so no trace of this must enter the reaction mixture.

EXPERIMENT

TO SHOW THAT SALIVA CONTAINS AN ENZYME THAT HYDROLYSES STARCH

TIME

This experiment takes about 45 minutes.

NON-KIT ITEMS

boiling water (from a kettle or saucepan)

cling film

cup or glass

detergent (for washing glassware)

household bleach (for cleaning glassware after the experiment)

indelible pen (to label pipettes and beakers)

white plate (or plate with white centre or back)

tablespoon

starch (e.g. arrowroot)

stop-watch or clock that displays seconds

paper tissues

KIT ITEMS

Chemical Tray

iodine

potassium iodide

Tray A

dropping pipettes (2)

glass stirring rod

test-tubes (2)

rubber teats for dropping pipettes (2)

Tray B

beakers, 100 cm³ (2)

Tray C

spatula

test-tube rack

Make sure you have good light where you intend to do the experiment. Read through all of the instructions and look at Figure 22 (p. 37) and Plate 3 before you start the experiment. *Note that, before doing the experiment, you must not eat for 15 minutes or smoke for one hour.*

You will need your Notebook and a pencil ready to record your results.

EXPERIMENTAL PROCEDURE

PART A: MAKING UP THE SOLUTIONS

Before you begin to do any of the experimental work wash all the glassware that you will be using thoroughly in hot water with detergent. Rinse it *well* in hot clean water and allow to drain.

The first part of the experiment involves making up *three* solutions. Ideally, you should have prepared the starch solution the day before you do the experiment. If your starch solution is in the fridge take it out now to allow it to come to room temperature.

Solution 1   Starch solution

Put a kettle (or saucepan) of water on to boil. Take a beaker, label it 'starch solution', and into it put one level spatula of starch (arrowroot). Fill a test-tube a quarter full of cold tap water and add this to the starch in the beaker. Stir until you have a white suspension. *Using water that is boiling as you pour*, almost fill the beaker and stir with the glass rod. A very hot, slightly cloudy solution of starch will be produced. Cover the beaker with cling film to keep out the dust and set it aside to cool. (Remember this solution must be at room temperature before you use it.)

Solution 2   Iodine/potassium iodide

Take a test-tube and place one level spatula of potassium iodide crystals in it. Add half a test-tube of cold tap water. Then carefully add two or three very small crystals of iodine. No more is needed. Shake the mixture until the particles of iodine have dissolved as far as possible. The final solution should have the colour of milkless tea. Place the test-tube in the test-tube rack.

Solution 3   Amylase solution

Measure a tablespoon of cold water into a cup or glass. Have ready a second beaker, label it 'enzyme,' and make sure you can see the stop-watch or clock that displays seconds. Take the water from the cup into your mouth and chew, swirl and gargle it vigorously for about 15 seconds. Now spit this solution into the beaker.

Your starch and enzyme solutions are clearly labelled, and it is important that they do not get mixed up. Put the three solutions that you have prepared to one side.

EXPERIMENT CONTINUED

PART B: TESTING THE AMYLASE

The following procedure is summarized in Figure 22 (on p. 37). You should also refer to Plate 3.

1 Have ready the clean, white plate. Take the dropping pipettes and label one A, the other B. Put a rubber teat on each pipette (it now operates like an 'eye dropper'). Using pipette A take in some of the iodine solution and put a ring of spots (about 9) of the solution around the plate. One or two drops per spot will be enough. (You may need to practise this!) Store pipette A in the test-tube containing the iodine solution in the test-tube rack, in case you need to repeat the experiment.

2 Pour about 1 cm depth of starch solution into a clean test-tube. Take dropping pipette B and, making sure you do not contaminate the end of the pipette with iodine solution, use the pipette to transfer a drop of this starch solution to an iodine drop on the plate. Mix the drops with the glass rod. Viewing the plate in bright light, note the grainy, dark blue spot. (It may look almost black.) This shows that starch is present.

3 Now add about a 2 cm depth of enzyme solution (i.e. your mouth washings) to the starch solution in the test-tube. Shake the mixture. Using pipette B, suck up a full pipette of this mixture. The enzyme reaction will go on inside the pipette. Make sure you can see the clock or stop-watch. Squeeze out one drop of the mixture on to successive iodine spots every 30 seconds. As soon as you have added the drop, note the colour. Go on doing this until addition of one drop of reaction mixture to a spot just fails to give a colour change. The total time that has elapsed since the enzyme was mixed with the starch is the achromatic time. Enter this time in your Notebook.

4 If you get no colour other than the original iodine colour after 30 seconds, then a great deal has happened very quickly. It means that in just 30 seconds all the amylose in the starch has been hydrolysed to dextrins and sugars by your amylase enzyme. In short, the achromatic time of your saliva solution is less than 30 seconds! Amylase is present at a high concentration in your saliva. If your saliva is as active as this and you wish to see the *progressive* hydrolysis of starch you can, if you have time, repeat the assay. You will need to dilute the mouth washings with more tap water. Dilute to about 50 cm³ (in the enzyme beaker) to start with, and then increase the dilution if necessary. Note the dilutions used.

5 If you see no colour change at all you may have inactive saliva (this is not uncommon) and you will need to note the colour changes in Plate 3 to appreciate the basis of this assay.

When you have completed the experiment discard all solutions down the sink and then pour down some household bleach. All glassware used must be completely immersed in some diluted household bleach solution overnight.

Warning Household bleach may be harmful and must be handled according to the manufacturer's instructions on the container.

Then rinse the glassware in clean hot water and allow to drain before putting back into the Kit.

The experiment may seem very crude and approximate—and, indeed, doing it in the way described above, it is! However, by using more accurate volume measurements, more sensitive ways of detecting the disappearance of the starch–iodine blue colour, and by careful regulation of the temperature and pH of the enzyme/substrate reaction mixture, the method can give reliable results. For many years, methods based on the starch–iodine reaction were used in clinical biochemistry to assay plasma amylase.

SUMMARY OF SECTION 4

1   Cells contain very many enzymes, most in solution but some in membranes. They are globular proteins but may contain a non-protein part. Each has a specific primary structure, and hence a specific higher-order structure. Each catalyses a specific reaction or type of reaction.

2   Enzymes have great catalytic power as can be seen by comparing the rates of a reaction with and without an enzyme. Catalysis occurs as a result of lowered activation energy. This is lowered as a consequence of the enzyme binding its substrate to an active site on the protein molecule. The enzyme–substrate complex breaks down to give product plus unchanged enzyme molecule. Specificity is also accounted for by enzyme-substrate complex formation. There is, to some extent for all enzymes, a lock and key relationship between enzyme active site and substrate molecule.

3   Metabolism is organized and regulated as a consequence of the specificity and relative activities of many different enzymes.

4   Variations in both temperature and pH affect the activity of enzymes. These effects have important physiological correlations.

5   Increasing temperature increases the rate of an enzyme-catalysed reaction until enzyme denaturation becomes the predominant process. As a result, activity increases up to a point and then falls off sharply.

6   Changes in pH alter the activity of an enzyme as a consequence of pH-induced changes in the R groups of certain amino acid residues. This affects weak bonding, hence higher-order structure, hence active site, hence activity. Each enzyme has a characteristic pH optimum.

7   The rate of any enzyme-catalysed reaction is proportional to the concentration of the enzyme, provided substrate concentration is in excess and temperature and pH are held constant. This relationship is the basis of enzyme assay, which is of great importance in clinical biochemistry.

8   Some enzyme-catalysed reactions depend on the presence of a particular coenzyme. NAD, FAD and coenzyme A are examples of coenzymes. Coenzymes are not proteins.

SAQ 17   An enzyme catalyses the dehydrogenation of compound BH_2 to B. The coenzyme NAD is also involved. The enzyme also has some activity with a different substrate JH_2, but at a rate only 10% of that with BH_2 as substrate. (a) What happens to the NAD in this dehydrogenation reaction? (b) What is the probable reason for the lower activity of the enzyme with JH_2?

SAQ 18   The pH optimum of one of the protease enzymes in the digestive system of a mammal is found to be 8. (a) What kind of reaction do you think this enzyme catalyses? (b) What differences would you expect there to be between the active site of this enzyme in a solution of pH 2 and in a solution of pH 8?

SAQ 19   The activity of enzyme Z in a sample of blood of pH 7.2 (sample A) is three times that in another sample of blood of pH 7.4 (sample B). What comments can you make about the relative amounts of Z in the two blood samples?

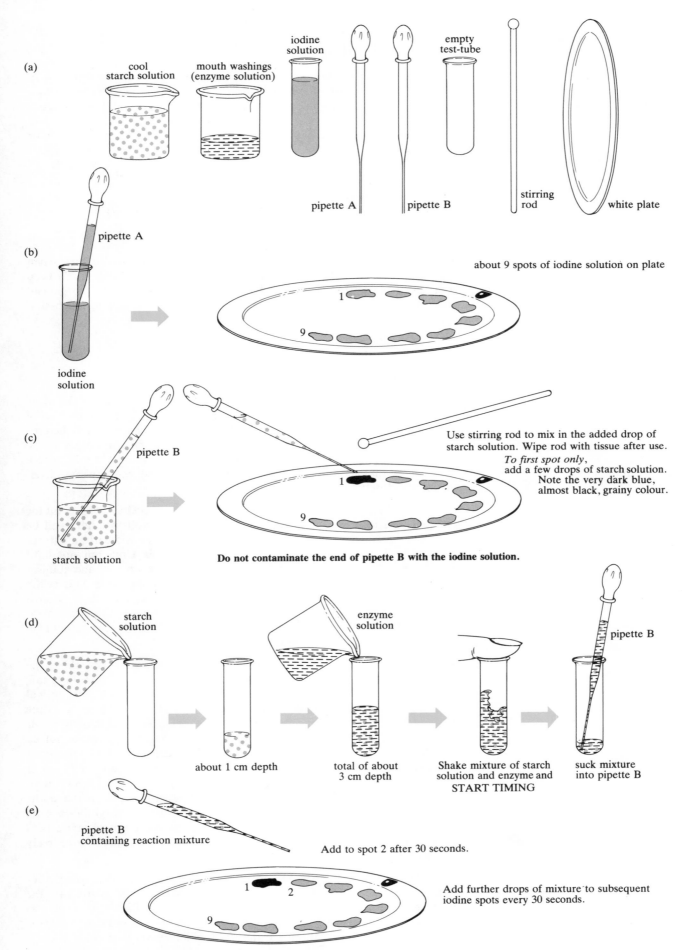

FIGURE 22   Experiment to demonstrate the activity of salivary amylase and to find the achromatic time. (see text p. 35)

5 OVERALL PROCESSES OF METABOLISM

From the text so far, you know something of the chemical constitution of cells and of the nature of metabolism as it relates to growth. In particular, you know that, at the molecular level of organization, biologists are concerned with the link between DNA and enzymes, with ATP production and utilization and with the acquisition and cellular deployment of precursor substances.

In the remainder of this Unit, the main focus of attention will be:

How is biochemistry investigated? (Section 5)
How is ATP made from ADP and P_i? (Sections 6 and 7)
How are organic compounds made? (Section 8)

This is a rather restricted view of biochemistry—necessarily so in an introductory text. As noted earlier, Unit 24 will take us somewhat further, when the story of DNA and protein synthesis is examined more closely. To keep some sense of perspective about what goes on in different kinds of organism and about how biochemical knowledge is obtained, the following discussion is important.

5.1 PERSPECTIVES

Look at Figure 23: a camel eating palm leaves. This encapsulates the ideas of autotrophism and heterotrophism developed earlier. It is a reminder of what biochemistry is about, and of the total dependence of the heterotrophic world upon autotrophs: no palm trees—no camels, in simple terms. This kind of ecological relationship is a major concern of Unit 25, where you will see that ecology and biochemistry (and, indeed, ecology and physiology) are closely linked.

Clearly, looking at the palm tree part of Figure 23, a good starting point for an excursion into the highways and byways of metabolism might well be photosynthesis—the primary process in terms of energy and carbon entrapment. We do indeed look into photosynthesis in this Unit, but not until Section 8.1. However, it is easier to begin with the area of metabolism common to all organisms, autotrophs and heterotrophs alike. This is the catabolism of organic compounds—animals eat them, fungi and heterotrophic bacteria absorb them and, of course, plants make them for themselves by photosynthesis. In Section 6 we shall look at glucose catabolism and in Section 7 at the catabolism of other compounds.

The schematic diagram of the camel and palm tree does not show the actual sites where these various metabolic processes occur. Those sites are, of course, the cells of their various tissues. Figure 24 shows a typical animal and plant cell, and is familiar to you from Unit 19 and the back of the biology Units. Some of the biochemical processes described shortly occur exclusively in the cytosol of each cell. This is the watery zone (of dissolved metabolites and enzymes) lying between the nucleus and membranous boundary of the cell. In solution in the cytosol, there occurs a range of important catabolic reactions. The **ribosomes**, mostly studded into convoluted membranous sheets of the **endoplasmic reticulum** that pervade the cytosol, are (as you know from Figure 2) the sites of protein synthesis. And, crucially important in the catabolic story, are the many **mitochondria** (singular mitochondrion) that, in contrast to ribosomes, are able to move freely in the cytosol (see Plates 4 and 5).

Cells differ in different tissues and in different organisms. But some components are common to the cells of all eukaryotes; in particular, the nucleus, cell membranes, cytosol, and mitochondria. Plants, however, as well as containing many mitochondria, also contain the organelles important in photosynthesis: these are the green **chloroplasts** that contain chlorophyll. You will learn more about these in Section 8.1.

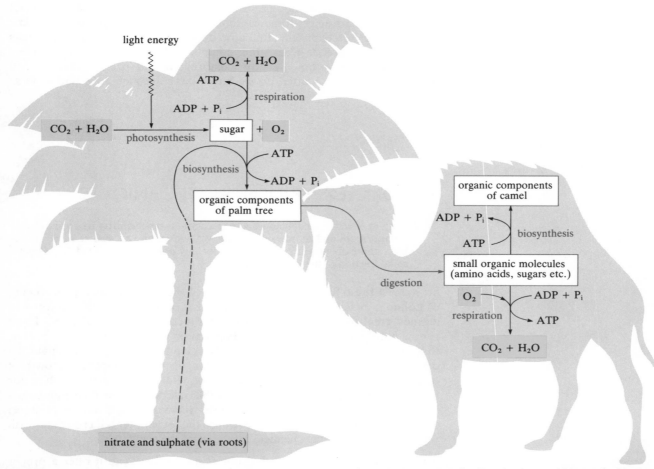

FIGURE 23   Heterotrophs digest and assimilate organic compounds made by autotrophs. Respiration and biosynthesis take place in both heterotrophs and autotrophs. The latter synthesize organic compounds (initially sugars) from carbon dioxide and water, using light energy.

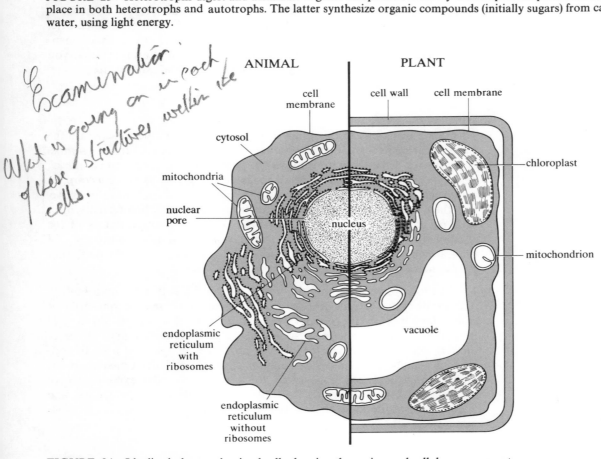

FIGURE 24   Idealized plant and animal cells showing the various subcellular components.

39

HOMOGENATE

CENTRIFUGE

ISOTOPIC LABELLING

The preceding discussion contains some bold assertions: protein synthesis occurs at the ribosomes; some catabolism occurs in the cytosol; and some occurs in the mitochondria. But how do we know? How do biochemists know anything precise about this complicated miniscule world of inter-linking pathways within the tiny membrane-bound packets that we call cells? How, for that matter, do we know there are metabolic pathways at all?

5.2 SOME EXPERIMENTAL TECHNIQUES

In spite of war-time difficulties and restrictions, biochemistry has continued to expand more and more rapidly each year, in stature as well as scope. It has been impossible for many years past for any one worker to read more than a small fraction of the new output. ...

So wrote Ernest Baldwin, then professor of biochemistry at the University of London, in January 1946! And if the rate of progress of the subject was deemed great then, it has been vastly and increasingly so ever since. There is now hardly a university, college, hospital or government, in any country, that does not have some part of its scientific activity that might be described as 'biochemical'. The reasons for this near exponential growth of biochemistry lay partly in its richness of unsolved problems (a lure for many scientists), partly in its demonstrable relevance to medicine and agri-culture, and partly because of the ever increasing availability of novel experimental techniques that provided the experimental crowbars with which to lever open the chemical mysteries of the cell.

This text is not a history of the subject nor, indeed, can it offer a proper review of biochemical methods. But, because biochemistry is so heavily dependent on quite sophisticated experimentation, and because reference is made to some techniques in the TV programme and in the text, some brief discussion will be useful. Remember, however, that the few methods men-tioned here are just a very small part of the experimental armoury that you would find in even quite modestly equipped biochemical laboratories.

Where in the cell?

To resolve questions of this kind, it is necessary to be able to separate the various parts of cells one from another—to be able to make from a sample of (say) liver cells, separate samples of 'pure cytosol', 'pure mitochondria', 'pure ribosomes' and so on. This depends on being able to make a soup, or **homogenate**, as it is more usually called, that is still biochemically active, and then being able to separate the components of this homogenate from each other by spinning it in a **centrifuge**. Extremely simple forms of the equipment used to effect such a separation are illustrated in the TV programme—the homogenizer being, as it is in many laboratories, very similar to an ordinary kitchen liquidizer.

A centrifuge (there are many different kinds, some with their own built-in refrigeration) has certain obvious resemblances to a domestic spin-drier: it spins—fast. Its capacity to separate components of cells depends on the fact that, when a homogenate is spun, the largest organelles and pieces of broken cell material reach the bottom of the centrifuge tube first. In con-trast, the smallest organelles can only be spun down if much greater speeds and spinning times are used. Again, this matches everyday experience with a spin-drier. Figure 25 shows the outline construction of a centrifuge, and Table 5 shows the kind of 'spin regime' needed to prepare some cell com-ponents.

FIGURE 25 (a) Construction of a simple centrifuge; (b) tubes of homogenate spinning in a centrifuge.

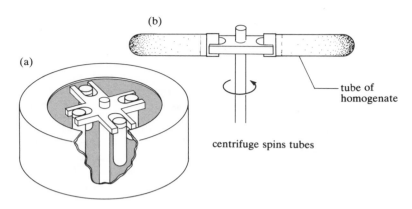

TABLE 5 Separation of subcellular components by centrifugation

Organelles	Duration of centrifugation/min	Ratio between magnitude of centrifugal acceleration and g*
nuclei	10	800
mitochondria	15	12 000
ribosomes	60	300 000

* This is related to the *speed* of centrifugation and is commonly referred to as 'so many g', for example $800\,g$ (where g is the magnitude of the acceleration due to gravity).

Following a pathway

Put yourself in the shoes of someone investigating the catabolism of glucose in the cytosol of yeast cells. The route, you believe from other work, can be represented thus (where A, B and C are unknown metabolites):

$$\text{glucose} \longrightarrow A \longrightarrow B \longrightarrow C \longrightarrow \text{pyruvic acid}$$

How could you identify A, B and C?

You learnt in Units 11–12 about isotopes. These are different forms of the same element. That is, they have the same atomic number but different mass number. The common form of carbon, constituting almost all the carbon atoms in natural cellular compounds, is ^{12}C. Suppose you were to prepare glucose containing substantial amounts of not ^{12}C but, instead, the radioactive isotope ^{14}C. Suppose you then supplied this to an active homogenate of yeast cells.

ITQ 6 What would you predict about the presence of ^{14}C in A, B, C and pyruvic acid in the above pathway?

This technique of **isotopic labelling**, as it is called, is widely used— in much more sophisticated and quantitative ways than outlined here—to follow the routes of metabolic pathways and so identify the intermediates along them.

Measuring respiration

As you might expect, you can hardly investigate the site, route and mechanism of oxidative catabolism within a cell unless you can *measure* the respiration that occurs. Remembering that the equation for glucose oxidation in cells is $C_6H_{12}O_6 + 6O_2 \longrightarrow 6CO_2 + 6H_2O$, it is easy to see that you could measure respiration rate by measuring either the rate at which oxygen is consumed or the rate at which carbon dioxide is produced. Both have been done by rather laborious but nevertheless reasonably accurate

41

OXYGEN ELECTRODE

methods involving measurements of pressure or volume changes in the space above a solution in which the reaction is occurring. In recent years, however, extensive use has been made of an electrochemical method of measuring the concentration of dissolved oxygen directly. The details need not concern us here; but, as the measurement of respiration rate using an **oxygen electrode** is shown in the TV programme, a brief discussion of this instrument is appropriate here.

The equipment layout and the kind of results produced are shown in Figure 26. Respiring material (a homogenate, cells, tissue or a small organism) is put in the chamber in an appropriate medium. (The chamber is carefully jacketed with circulating water of a controlled temperature.) Substances—for example, possible metabolites to be tested—can be added into the sealed chamber through a small hole in the top. An electrical signal whose strength is directly proportional to the oxygen concentration inside the chamber is generated by a special electrode on the floor of the chamber. The signal is amplified and led to a chart recorder which plots a graph of oxygen concentration against time, and from this trace respiration rates may be read off directly.

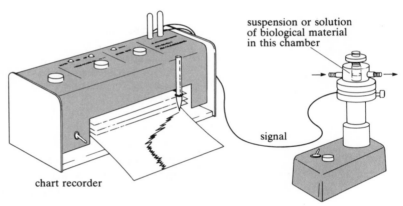

FIGURE 26 Oxygen electrode assembly. The electrode itself is made of platinum. As oxygen is used, the concentration of dissolved oxygen in the chamber falls. This produces a signal which, after amplification, is registered by a movement of the pen on the graph paper of the chart recorder. The chamber is kept at constant temperature by water circulated through the jacket surrounding the chamber (see arrows).

suspension or solution of biological material in this chamber

signal

chart recorder

SUMMARY OF SECTION 5

1 Autotrophs and heterotrophs have a biochemical and consequent ecological relationship with each other.

2 Catabolism occurs in all cells of plants and animals. Some catabolic processes take place in the cytosol and some in the mitochondria.

3 Protein synthesis is an anabolic process common to cells of both plants and animals, and occurs at the ribosomes. Photosynthesis (in plants) takes place in the chloroplasts.

4 The rapid advance in biochemical research has depended on the emergence of suitable experimental techniques. Among the most important are homogenization, centrifugation, isotopic labelling and measurement of respiration rates.

5 Centrifugation is a separation technique depending on the different responses of cell components (in a homogenate) to different regimes of spin speed and spin time.

6 Isotopic labelling involves replacement of the more usual atoms in a cellular compound with unusual isotopes (often radioactive). In this way, the fate of the labelled compound can be followed.

7 Respiration rates can be measured with an oxygen electrode.

SAQ 20 Glucose is catabolized to carbon dioxide and water via pyruvic acid. The route can be represented in two parts:

(a) glucose ⟶ pyruvic acid

(b) pyruvic acid + oxygen ⟶ carbon dioxide + water

If route (a) occurs in the cytosol only, whereas route (b) occurs in the mitochondria only, which of the following results would you expect to find experimentally?

(i) Glucose labelled with ^{14}C would yield $^{14}CO_2$ when added to an oxygenated homogenate of liver cells.

(ii) Glucose labelled with ^{14}C would yield $^{14}CO_2$ when added to a homogenate from which all oxygen had been excluded.

(iii) In an oxygen electrode assembly, addition of glucose to a suspension of active mitochondria in a cytosol-free suspension would lead to some oxygen consumption.

6 CATABOLISM OF CARBOHYDRATES

Carbohydrates, you may remember from Section 3.3, include sugars such as glucose and sucrose (table sugar), and polysaccharides such as starch and glycogen. We shall be concerned almost exclusively with glucose catabolism, as glucose is the form in which almost all carbohydrate enters cells and into which almost all forms of carbohydrate are converted. When you eat, carbohydrate is digested largely to monosaccharides which, after absorption in the intestine, are transported to the liver. In the liver, other dietary monosaccharides such as fructose are biochemically converted to glucose and any temporary excess of glucose is stored as glycogen. That store is used to maintain blood glucose between meals at levels sufficient to supply cells in all parts of the body with oxidizable fuel. (We return to carbohydrate storage and the regulation of blood glucose again in Unit 23.)

As you will see in Section 7, cells also catabolize fat and amino acids, but glucose is a major fuel in all cells and for some tissues, notably the brain, is the *only* acceptable fuel. Maintenance of blood glucose and glucose catabolism are, therefore, rather important! And, with some differences in detail, glucose has an essential catabolic role in other animals, in bacteria and, not surprisingly, in plants too—being, in the latter, the photosynthetically produced fuel.

This Section is, therefore, much concerned with the detail of *how* glucose is catabolized to produce ATP. Though the route may seem complicated, it is noteworthy that the pathways by which fatty acids, glycerol and amino acids are catabolized share substantial parts of the pathway by which glucose is catabolized to carbon dioxide and water. Many for the price of one, in terms of learning effort! Figure 27 makes the point pictorially.

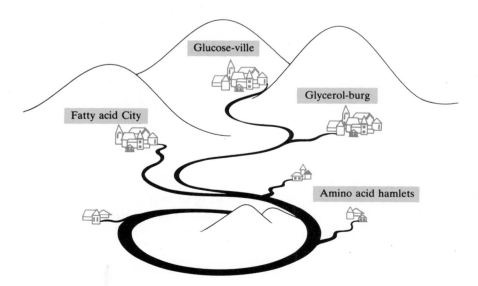

FIGURE 27 Other pathways, from fatty acids, glycerol and amino acids, join the glucose road.

6.1 AN OVERVIEW OF GLUCOSE CATABOLISM

As you know, the complete oxidation of glucose is represented by the equation: $C_6H_{12}O_6 + 6O_2 \longrightarrow 6CO_2 + 6H_2O$. This is what happens when you burn glucose on a spoon, and it is what happens, overall, in the cells of an organism. In both cases—in the fire on the spoon and in the sequence of reactions at constant temperature *in vivo*—some 3 000 kJ of chemical energy are released per mole of glucose oxidized. This equivalence is shown very simply in Figure 28.

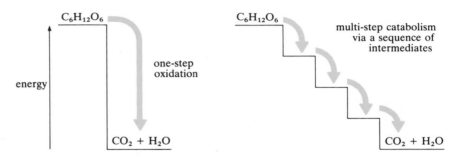

FIGURE 28   The catabolism of glucose in steps leads to the production of the same amount of energy as in the one-step oxidation.

☐ Into what form is that chemical energy converted when glucose is burned on the spoon? Into what form is it converted when glucose is oxidized *in vivo*?

■ On the spoon, all the energy appears as heat. *In vivo*, some appears as heat and some as chemical energy in the ATP molecules formed from ADP and P_i.

ITQ 7   In Section 2.3 you learnt that making a mole of ATP from ADP and P_i requires around 30 kJ. It is an experimental fact that when one mole of glucose is completely catabolized to carbon dioxide and water a total of 38 moles of ATP are made. Given that the complete oxidation of a mole of glucose makes about 3 000 kJ of energy available, calculate: (a) how many kilojoules of heat are initially produced in glucose catabolism; (b) the percentage of the chemical energy available from glucose oxidation that is initially converted into the chemical energy of ATP.

So, the overall catabolism of glucose must amount to the overall equation noted above; and, moreover, we should expect to see 38 molecules of ATP produced *en route* for each molecule of glucose catabolized. The route as a whole consists of four smaller sets of metabolic reactions spread over both cytosol and mitochondria. The overall route is extremely daunting in appearance and you do not need to know it, except in outline. But since we refer to it several times in both this and the following Sections, it is given here as Figure 29. The Figure is included for interest only—you do *not* need to learn the details.

What you do need to know are the names and key features of the four component pathways and where they occur in cells. Those pathways, in the order in which they operate, are glycolysis (also known as the glycolytic pathway), the link reaction, the tricarboxylic acid cycle (abbreviated to TCA cycle) and, finally, the electron transport chain (ETC, for short).

Glycolysis

Imagine that a glucose molecule has just entered the cell, and catabolism begins. The first stage is **glycolysis** ('glyco-lysis' means glucose splitting), and this occurs entirely in the cytosol. The overall result is that each glucose

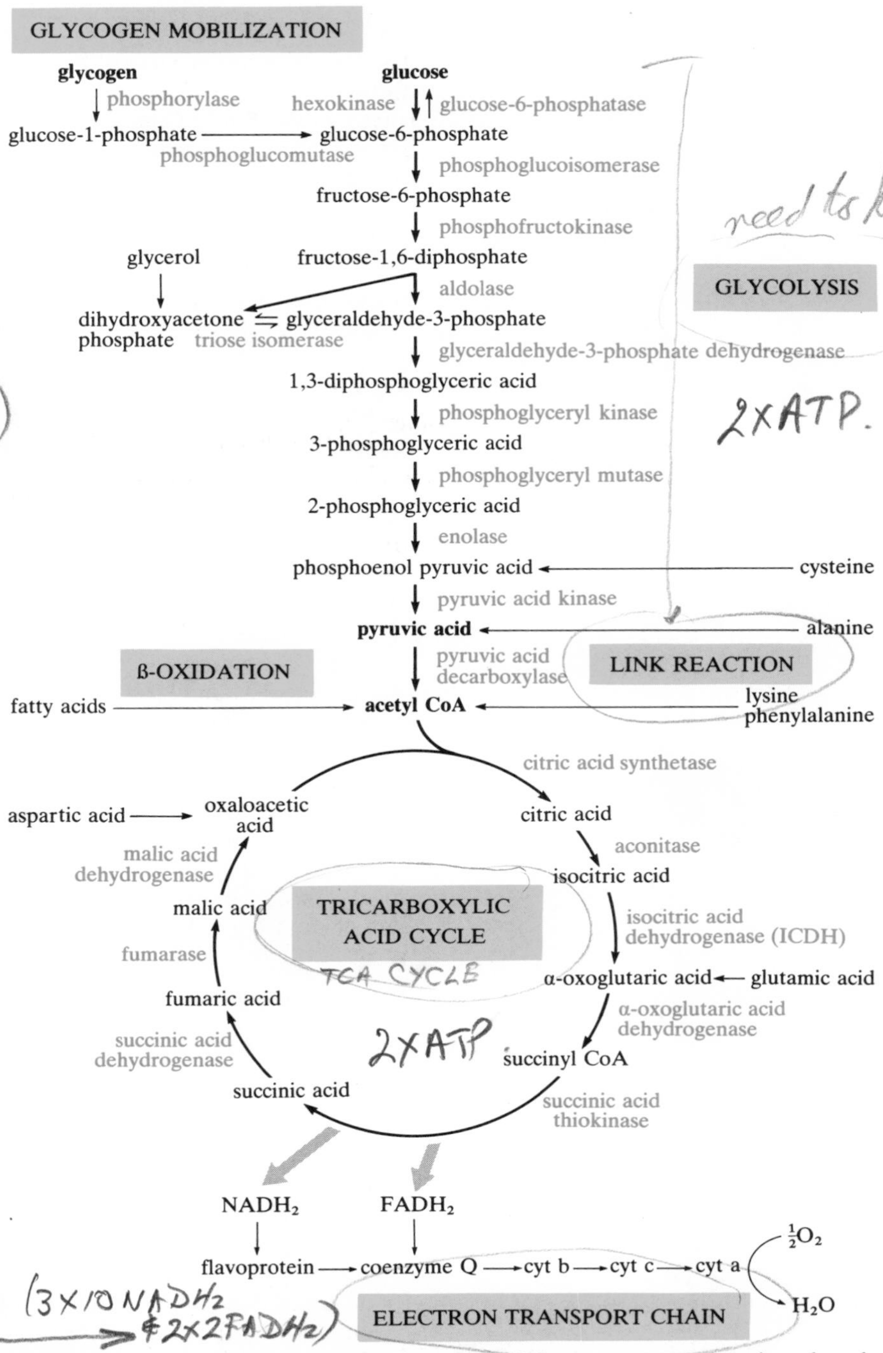

(Handwritten margin notes:)

GLYCOGEN MOBILIZATION

GLYCOLYSIS ①

LINK REACTION ②

TCA CYCLE
(TRICARBOXYLIC ACID CYCLE ③)

β OXIDATION

ETC ⓐ

(Handwritten: "need to know!")

GLYCOGEN MOBILIZATION

glycogen → (phosphorylase) glucose-1-phosphate → (phosphoglucomutase) glucose-6-phosphate

glucose → (hexokinase / glucose-6-phosphatase) glucose-6-phosphate

glucose-6-phosphate → (phosphoglucoisomerase) fructose-6-phosphate → (phosphofructokinase) fructose-1,6-diphosphate → (aldolase)

glycerol → dihydroxyacetone phosphate ⇌ glyceraldehyde-3-phosphate (triose isomerase)

GLYCOLYSIS *(handwritten: 2 X ATP.)*

glyceraldehyde-3-phosphate → (glyceraldehyde-3-phosphate dehydrogenase) 1,3-diphosphoglyceric acid → (phosphoglyceryl kinase) 3-phosphoglyceric acid → (phosphoglyceryl mutase) 2-phosphoglyceric acid → (enolase) phosphoenol pyruvic acid ← cysteine → (pyruvic acid kinase) pyruvic acid ← alanine

LINK REACTION

pyruvic acid → (pyruvic acid decarboxylase) acetyl CoA ← lysine, phenylalanine

β-OXIDATION

fatty acids → acetyl CoA

acetyl CoA → (citric acid synthetase) citric acid → (aconitase) isocitric acid → (isocitric acid dehydrogenase (ICDH)) α-oxoglutaric acid ← glutamic acid → (α-oxoglutaric acid dehydrogenase) succinyl CoA → (succinic acid thiokinase) succinic acid → (succinic acid dehydrogenase) fumaric acid → (fumarase) malic acid → (malic acid dehydrogenase) oxaloacetic acid ← aspartic acid → citric acid

TRICARBOXYLIC ACID CYCLE *(handwritten: TCA CYCLE, 2 X ATP)*

NADH₂, FADH₂ → flavoprotein → coenzyme Q → cyt b → cyt c → cyt a → ½O₂ / H₂O

ELECTRON TRANSPORT CHAIN

(Handwritten: 34 X ATP (3×10 NADH₂ + 2×2 FADH₂))

FIGURE 29 Catabolism in detail. The names of the enzymes are given in red, and the important component metabolic pathways are highlighted in pink. (*Note:* This Figure is for reference—you do *not* need to learn the details.)

molecule is split by a series of reactions into two molecules of pyruvic acid, and two pairs of hydrogen atoms that are collected by two molecules of the coenzyme NAD. Thus the overall process of glycolysis is:

$$C_6H_{12}O_6 + 2NAD \longrightarrow 2CH_3COCOOH + 2NADH_2$$

glucose   pyruvic acid

Note: (i) $CH_3COCOOH$ is a shorthand form of the fuller structural formula of pyruvic acid (given in Table 1). In fact, from hereon you will find that a number of formulae have been abbreviated in this way—as is conventional in many biochemistry texts.

(ii) Pyruvic acid is ionized as the pyruvate ion (CH_3COCOO^-) at cellular pH. Biochemists often refer to pyruvic acid and pyruvate interchangeably.

The link reaction

The **link reaction** occurs in the fluid-filled centre, called the matrix, of each mitochondrion. In this reaction (catalysed by a large complex enzyme dissolved in the fluid of the matrix), the two pyruvic acid molecules that have entered from the cytosol are converted to two acetic acid molecules. The overall reaction is given below.

$$2CH_3COCOOH + 2NAD \longrightarrow 2CH_3COOH + 2NADH_2 + 2CO_2$$
$$\text{pyruvic acid} \qquad\qquad\qquad\qquad \text{acetic acid}$$

Notice that once again hydrogen atoms are removed, transferred as before to the coenzyme NAD. This equation is a simplification: the true product is *not* acetic acid, as such, but a compound of acetic acid and another coenzyme called **coenzyme A**. The compound is termed **acetyl coenzyme A** —abbreviated to **acetyl CoA**. In this introductory text, we shall use the names acetyl CoA and acetic acid interchangeably: we can therefore equally well write the link reaction as*:

$$2CH_3COCOOH + 2NAD + 2CoA$$
$$\text{pyruvic acid} \qquad\qquad \longrightarrow 2 \text{ acetyl CoA} + 2NADH_2 + 2CO_2$$

The tricarboxylic acid cycle

The fluid of the mitochondrial matrix also contains a number of enzymes that catalyse a circular sequence of reactions called the **tricarboxylic acid cycle** (often abbreviated to **TCA cycle**). In ways that will become clearer in the AV sequence that follows shortly, one turn of this cycle converts each acetyl CoA molecule to carbon dioxide and several pairs of hydrogen atoms that are once again collected by coenzymes. As usual, NAD is converted to $NADH_2$; this time, however, another coenzyme (FAD: see Table 4) is also involved, being converted to $FADH_2$. Because *two* molecules of acetyl CoA are produced from each glucose molecule, the cycle has to turn *twice* to deal with them. (Some people remember this idea by thinking of the TCA cycle as the 'TCA *bi*cycle'!)

Thus, the overall reaction accomplished by two turns of the TCA cycle is

$$2 \text{ acetyl CoA} + 6NAD + 2FAD$$
$$\longrightarrow 4CO_2 + 6NADH_2 + 2FADH_2$$

The electron transport chain

If you scan the equations in the previous paragraphs you will see that from one molecule of glucose, a good many molecules of reduced coenzymes have been produced.

☐ Some of them are $NADH_2$ and some are $FADH_2$. Look at the relevant equations and count up how many there are of each.

■ There are 10 molecules of $NADH_2$ and 2 molecules of $FADH_2$. ($2NADH_2$ are produced in glycolysis, $2NADH_2$ in the link reaction and $6NADH_2$ in two turns of the TCA cycle. The $2FADH_2$ are produced in the TCA cycle, one per turn.)

What happens to all these molecules of reduced coenzymes? The answer is that they are re-oxidized in the **electron transport chain** (ETC for short),

---

* Because of the simplifications introduced, neither of the equations used here to represent the link reaction is balanced. This does not matter—'approximate representations' are often used in biochemical texts.

with dissolved oxygen as the oxidizing agent. The enzymes that bring about this vital oxidative process are insoluble membrane-bound proteins, fixed into the folded inner membrane of each mitochondrion: Figure 30 shows the structure of a mitochondrion in diagrammatic form, and Plate 5 is an

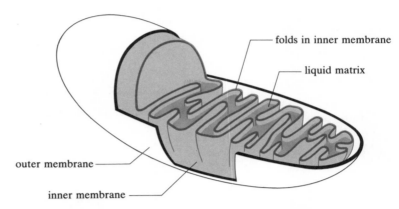

FIGURE 30   Diagram of a mitochondrion. The inner membrane, containing the enzymes of the electron transport chain, is shown in red. Mitochondria are typically about 10 μm long.

electron micrograph of one mitochondrion in a mouse cell. The overall reaction accomplished in the electron transport chain per glucose molecule is therefore:

$$10NADH_2 + 2FADH_2 + 6O_2 \longrightarrow 10NAD + 2FAD + 12H_2O$$

The four stages acting in concert

These four stages act together to bring about the complete catabolism of glucose to carbon dioxide and water. In the process they make 38 ATP molecules by ways to be discussed shortly. But first look at Figure 31 which shows the stages fitted together in outline form.

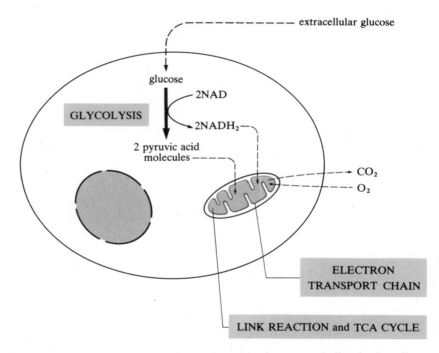

FIGURE 31   Location of the four stages of aerobic glucose catabolism in the cell.

6.2 A BALANCED EQUATION

This Section consists mainly of the AV sequence, which you will find on Tape 4 (Side 1, Band 1). Its main purpose is to revise the ideas introduced in the outline above, and also to convince you that the overall equation for glucose oxidation as it occurs on a spoon is *exactly* that which occurs in the somewhat tortuous routes of catabolism. Some new ideas are introduced; in particular, the production of the 38 ATPs per glucose is explained in some detail. You should work through the AV sequence now.

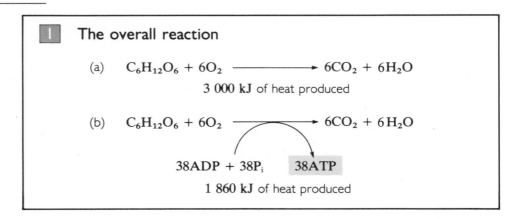

1 The overall reaction

(a) $C_6H_{12}O_6 + 6O_2 \longrightarrow 6CO_2 + 6H_2O$

3 000 kJ of heat produced

(b) $C_6H_{12}O_6 + 6O_2 \longrightarrow 6CO_2 + 6H_2O$

$38ADP + 38P_i$ → 38ATP

1 860 kJ of heat produced

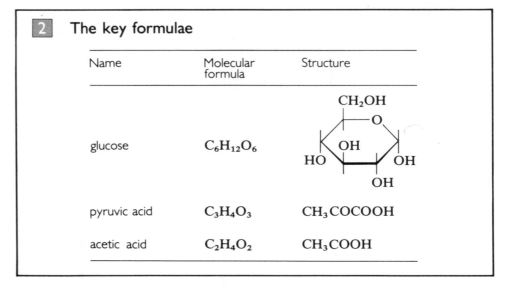

2 The key formulae

Name	Molecular formula	Structure
glucose	$C_6H_{12}O_6$	(structure shown)
pyruvic acid	$C_3H_4O_3$	$CH_3COCOOH$
acetic acid	$C_2H_4O_2$	CH_3COOH

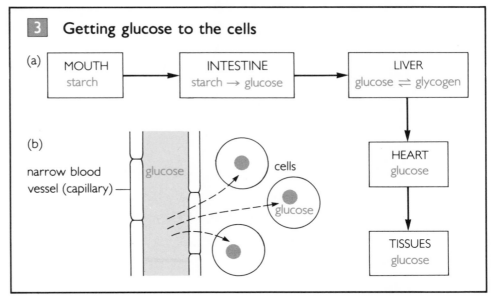

3 Getting glucose to the cells

(a)

MOUTH
starch
→
INTESTINE
starch → glucose
→
LIVER
glucose ⇌ glycogen
↓
HEART
glucose
↓
TISSUES
glucose

(b)

narrow blood vessel (capillary)
glucose
cells
glucose

4 Glycolysis: balancing the atoms

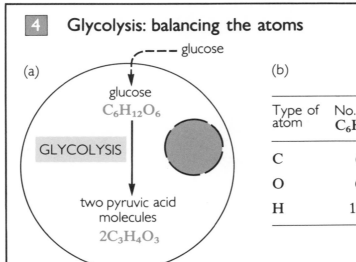

(a)

(b)

Type of atom	No. in $C_6H_{12}O_6$	No. in $2C_3H_4O_3$	Change
C	6	6	none
O	6	....	....
H	12	....	....

5 Glycolysis: $NADH_2$ and ATP production

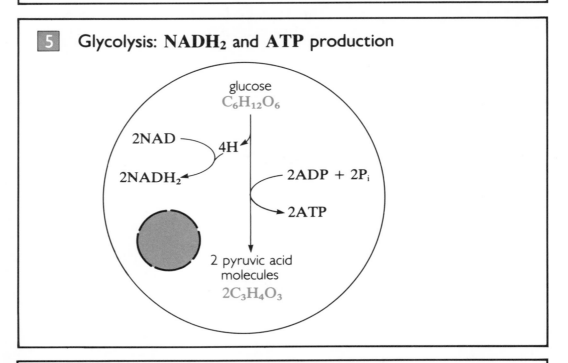

6 Summary Table: changes that occur when one molecule of glucose is catabolized

	ATP produced by substrate level phosphorylation	$NADH_2$ produced	CO_2 produced	H_2O 'lent'	$FADH_2$ produced
GLYCOLYSIS					
LINK REACTION					
TCA CYCLE					
GRAND TOTAL					

7 **The link reaction**

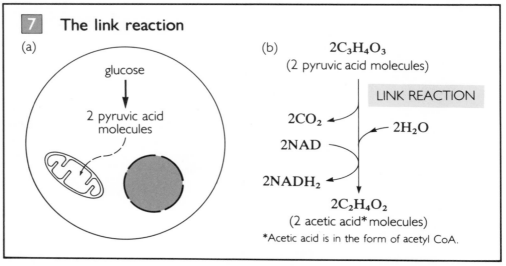

(a)

glucose

2 pyruvic acid
molecules

(b)

$2C_3H_4O_3$
(2 pyruvic acid molecules)

LINK REACTION

$2CO_2$

$2H_2O$

$2NAD$

$2NADH_2$

$2C_2H_4O_2$
(2 acetic acid* molecules)

*Acetic acid is in the form of acetyl CoA.

8 **The TCA cycle: its relationship to earlier stages in glucose catabolism**

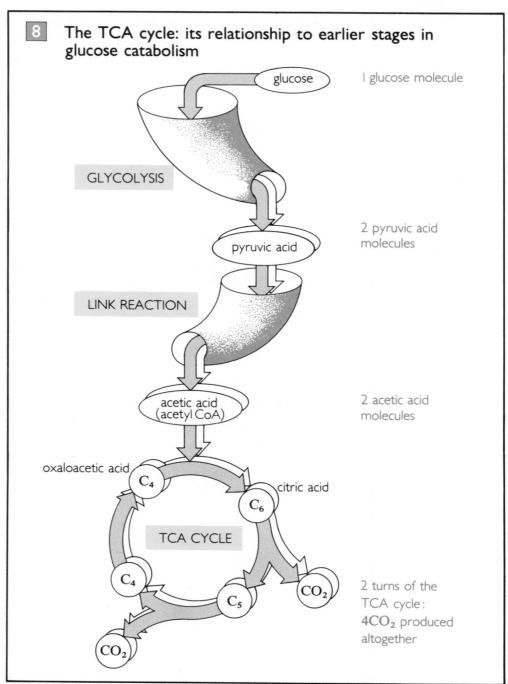

glucose — I glucose molecule

GLYCOLYSIS

pyruvic acid — 2 pyruvic acid molecules

LINK REACTION

acetic acid (acetyl CoA) — 2 acetic acid molecules

oxaloacetic acid — C_4

citric acid — C_6

TCA CYCLE

C_4

C_5

CO_2

CO_2

2 turns of the TCA cycle: $4CO_2$ produced altogether

9 The TCA cycle: atom balance

(a) $C_2H_4O_2 \longrightarrow 2CO_2$
acetic acid

(b) $C_2H_4O_2 + \ldots\ldots H_2O \longrightarrow 2CO_2 + \ldots\ldots H$
(hydrogen atoms carried by coenzymes)

10 One turn of the TCA cycle: the products

$$2H_2O \qquad ADP + P_i \qquad ATP$$

$$C_2H_4O_2 \xrightarrow{\hspace{6cm}} 2CO_2$$
acetic acid

$$3NAD \qquad 3NADH_2$$
$$FAD \qquad FADH_2$$

for two turns of the TCA cycle multiply everything by 2

11 Achievement so far compared with overall goal

(a) Achievement so far:

$$C_6H_{12}O_6 + 6H_2O \xrightarrow{\hspace{8cm}} 6CO_2$$

$$10NAD \quad 10NADH_2 \quad 4ADP \quad 4ATP$$
$$2FAD \quad 2FADH_2 \quad + 4P_i$$

(b) Overall goal:

$$C_6H_{12}O_6 + 6O_2 \xrightarrow{\hspace{8cm}} 6CO_2 + 6H_2O$$

$$38ADP \quad 38ATP$$
$$+ 38P_i$$

12 The electron transport chain

(a)

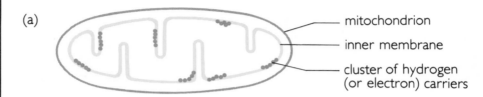

mitochondrion

inner membrane

cluster of hydrogen
(or electron) carriers

(b) $NADH_2 + \frac{1}{2}O_2 \longrightarrow NAD + H_2O$

$FADH_2 + \frac{1}{2}O_2 \longrightarrow FAD + H_2O$

(c)

$NADH_2$ $\frac{1}{2}O_2$

NAD   hydrogen atoms (or electrons) H_2O
are passed down a linear sequence of carriers

Note: a hydrogen atom is equivalent to a hydrogen ion (H^+) plus an electron (e^-).

13 Oxidative phosphorylation

(a) $NADH_2$ $\frac{1}{2}O_2$

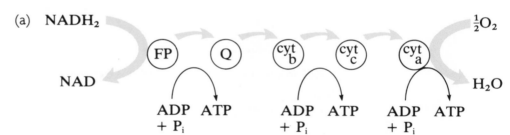

NAD H_2O

ADP ATP   ADP ATP   ADP ATP
+ P_i + P_i + P_i

3ATP per molecule of $NADH_2$ oxidized

(b) $FADH_2$ $\frac{1}{2}O_2$

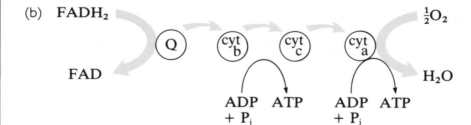

FAD H_2O

ADP ATP   ADP ATP
+ P_i + P_i

2ATP per molecule of $FADH_2$ oxidized

14 The ATP tally

In the catabolism of one molecule of glucose:

(a) ☐ How many molecules of **ATP** are produced in the oxidation of 10 $NADH_2$?

■ ....

☐ How many molecules of **ATP** are produced in the oxidation of 2 $FADH_2$?

■ ....

(b) ☐ How many molecules of **ATP** are produced by oxidative phosphorylation?

■ ....

☐ How many molecules of **ATP** are produced by substrate level phosphorylation?

■ ....

☐ What is the *total* number of **ATP** molecules produced?

■ ....

15 Summary

(a) $C_6H_{12}O_6 + 6H_2O + 4ADP + 4P_i \rightarrow 6CO_2 + 12$ pairs of H atoms $+ 4ATP$

(by SL phos)

(b) 12 pairs of H atoms $+ 6O_2 + 34ADP + 34P_i \rightarrow 12H_2O + 34ATP$

(by ox phos)

(c) $C_6H_{12}O_6 + 6O_2 + 38ADP + 38P_i \rightarrow 6CO_2 + 6H_2O + 38ATP$

You should now be convinced that the four linked stages of glucose catabolism add up, in chemical equation terms, to $C_6H_{12}O_6 + 6O_2 \longrightarrow 6CO_2 + 6H_2O$, with the associated formation of 38 ATPs. The metabolic detail on which this exercise is based was worked out by years of experimental work between the mid-1930s and (as far as details of oxidative phosphorylation are concerned) much more recent years.

☐ Why do you think that the catabolism is so spread out over so many reactions? Why do you think the oxidation of the reduced coenzymes occurs over many steps in the electron transport chain?

■ The very large amount of chemical energy made available by complete glucose oxidation must be utilized in ways that are controllable and that do not lead to a rate of heat production that would raise the temperature and put the cellular proteins at risk. Thus, the 'small packets' approach to energy transduction is one that you might have expected to have evolved.

As you learned from the AV sequence, making ATP from ADP and P_i is called phosphorylation, and there are two types. One of these does not depend directly on oxygen itself and, because the actual metabolites involved contain phosphate groups that are transferred onto ADP to give ATP, that process is termed substrate level phosphorylation. The other kind of phosphorylation occurs solely in the electron transport chain and therefore depends crucially on the presence of oxygen. Not surprisingly, making ATP this way is called oxidative phosphorylation. You will recall from the AV sequence that of the 38 ATPs made per glucose molecule catabolized, four are produced by substrate level phosphorylation* and 34 by oxidative phosphorylation. Little more will be said about the former—it happens in glycolysis and the TCA cycle, as you know—but oxidative phosphorylation will be explored further in Section 6.3. Figure 32 gives an outline summary that (unlike Figure 29!) you should become familiar with.

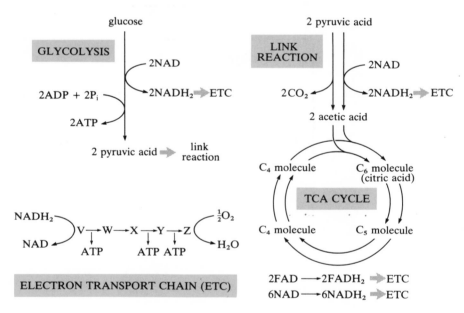

FIGURE 32 Summary of glycolysis, link reaction, TCA cycle and electron transport chain showing the relationship between these stages. (Note that four CO_2 molecules are produced in the two turns of the TCA cycle shown here.)

* This number is the *net* ATP production from one molecule of glucose. If you examined the details of catabolism you would see that in some catabolic reactions ATP is actually *used*. However, more is produced in later reactions, resulting in a net ATP gain.

6.3 MITOCHONDRIA: THE POWERHOUSES OF THE CELL

Different kinds of cell have different numbers of mitochondria within them, sometimes more than a thousand per cell. The more work the cells do (of whatever kind: see Section 2.3) the more mitochondria they contain. Thus, for example, a living skin cell contains many fewer mitochondria than a muscle cell or a liver cell. Skin cells are relatively passive metabolically, whereas both muscle and liver cells are involved in the expenditure of much kinetic or biosynthetic energy (muscles contract, liver cells synthesize many chemicals). Thus the ATP requirements of cells vary, and consequently the number of mitochondria they possess also differs.

As you know, most of the ATP produced in mitochondria is made by oxidative phosphorylation. It is well worth remembering that almost all the oxygen you take in via your lungs is channelled to the billions of mitochondria in your body. Put another way, it is the activity of oxygen-using carbon dioxide-producing mitochondria that makes you breathe. You will learn about the physiological effect and detail of this in Unit 23.

The precise point at which oxygen itself is involved is right at the end of the sequence of alternately oxidized and reduced substances that make up the electron transport chain. Figure 33 shows a simplified version of the ETC, including the three ATP-making points (remember from the AV sequence that 3 ATPs per $NADH_2$ are made). As you see in Figure 33a, $NADH_2$ donates its pair of hydrogens to a flavoprotein carrier (FP) and thence to another coenzyme (coenzyme Q) which becomes reduced to QH_2. This kind of alternate reduction/reoxidation then follows all down the length of the chain.

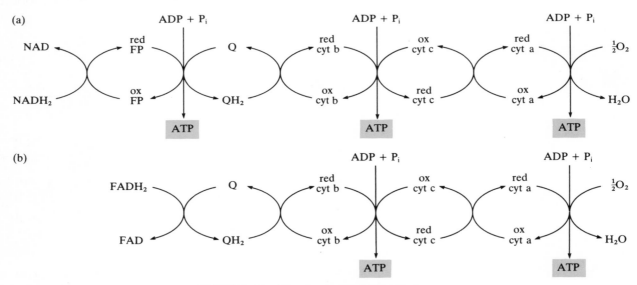

FIGURE 33   The electron transport chain.

Figure 33b shows the route for $FADH_2$ oxidation via the ETC: notice here that only 2 ATPs are made. As you saw, this difference in ATP production between $NADH_2$ and $FADH_2$ helps account for the 38 ATP total.

Many of the ETC components are iron-containing proteins called **cytochromes**, the iron atom within each cytochrome molecule being alternately reduced to iron(II) and oxidized to iron(III). The final component of the chain is cytochrome a, and the reduced form of this is re-oxidized by molecular oxygen. (Interestingly, cytochrome a is irreversibly inhibited by cyanide ions (CN^-), which is why potassium cyanide and other cyanide compounds are so poisonous.)

This description of the electron transport chain with its associated oxidative phosphorylation is a very simplified one—exactly *how* ATP is made by the progression of oxidation/reduction reactions from $NADH_2/NAD$ or $FADH_2/FAD$ at one end to O_2/H_2O at the other has long been the subject of active and contentious research. The theory for which there is most evidence, and for which Peter Mitchell (its chief proponent) was awarded a Nobel Prize, is explained in outline below.

A discussion of Mitchell's theory depends on the fact that the ETC does not, for most of its length, transport hydrogen *atoms* at all. Rather, it ejects a hydrogen ion and then transports the electron that remains. The relationship between atom, ion and electron is, as you know, simply:

$$H \longrightarrow H^+ + e^-$$

It is the latter that is transported, hence the name electron transport chain.

According to Mitchell's model, the H^+ ions produced as a consequence of removing electrons from neutral hydrogen atoms behave in the following way. As the H^+ ions are produced by the proteins of the ETC (chemically bound in linear sets attached to the inner mitochondrial membrane), they are discharged to the *outside* of the inner membrane. Thus, *the concentration of H^+ ions on the outside becomes progressively greater than the concentrations of H^+ ions within the mitochondrial matrix.* Thus a concentration gradient of H^+ ions is formed as a result of electron transport. This is shown in Figure 34a.

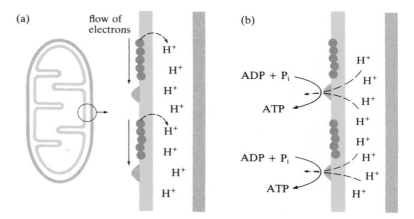

FIGURE 34 (a) The flow of electrons along the array of ETC components leads to increased H^+ concentration on the outside of the inner membrane. Two of the many 'sets' of ETC components are shown (the chains of red circles). In (b), the H^+ ions flow back into the matrix down the concentration gradient through a special ATP-making complex (shown as grey bumps) on the inside of the inner mitochondrial membrane.

In Section 2.3 you met the idea that pumping ions against a concentration gradient requires the expenditure of energy. The process, termed active transport, was likened to pumping water up a hill: active transport requires, you may remember, the conversion of ATP to ADP and P_i. It is not hard to appreciate the reverse process. If the mitochondrion *creates a gradient of H^+ ions* in the way described above and then allows those ions to *flow back down the concentration gradient* (like water running down hill), the energy made available as a result can be conserved by *making ATP from ADP and P_i*—that is, by phosphorylation! This is shown in Figure 34b.

Though there is a good deal of experimental evidence for an ATP-synthesizing mechanism of the kind postulated by Mitchell, many of the details remain to be discovered.

6.4 SURVIVING WITHOUT OXYGEN

A good many microbes can live without oxygen and some are actually destroyed by oxygen. *Clostridium tetani*, the causative organism of tetanus, is one rather nasty example. Others can live with or without oxygen, adapting their life-style to suit the environment. One familiar example is yeast. Aerobically it does everything described earlier but, in the absence of oxygen, it resorts to **anaerobic respiration**.

The absence of oxygen has a profound effect, for no ETC activity is possible at all. And, because there are only a few micrograms of the hydrogen-carrying coenzymes NAD and FAD in each cell, you might expect that cessation of electron transport in mitochondria would lead to the conversion of all the NAD to $NADH_2$ and all the FAD to $FADH_2$. Were that to happen, metabolism would cease, ATP production would cease, and anaerobism would be synonymous with death! As the following discussion shows, the scene is not so bleak as that.

What yeast does in the absence of oxygen is to use a compound formed from pyruvate (the end-product of glycolysis) to reoxidize the two $NADH_2$ molecules produced in glycolysis. In so doing, NAD is regenerated, and so glycolysis can continue. In addition, a small amount of ATP is made (via the catabolism of glucose to pyruvate) thereby sustaining life. Two steps are involved. Firstly pyruvate is decarboxylated (carbon dioxide is removed) by the enzyme **pyruvate decarboxylase**. The product of the reaction is acetaldehyde, and this in turn is reduced by $NADH_2$ to give ethanol plus NAD. This latter reaction is catalysed by the enzyme alcohol dehydrogenase.* The anaerobic catabolism of glucose to ethanol (also called **fermentation**) is a process that occurs in every brewery or wine vat. It is summarized in Figure 35.

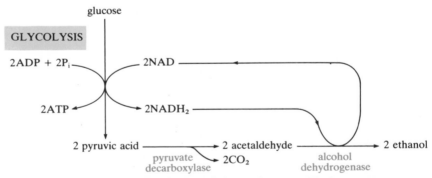

FIGURE 35   Anaerobic catabolism of glucose in yeast. (The key enzymes are shown in red.)

Anaerobic respiration can also occur in our own muscles. The yield of ATP, like that in yeast, is only two per glucose molecule. However, the possibility that this affords of allowing muscles to continue to contract *even though they have exhausted all their supplies of oxygen* is invaluable, say, in the 100 metres dash or in running for a bus. In evolutionary terms, this may well have been an adaptation to the 'hunt and flee' life of our distant ancestors.

* You met this enzyme on p. 31; there you saw that it catalyses the reverse reaction (ethanol ⟶ acetaldehyde) in the liver.

Biochemically, the situation is similar to that in yeast but rather simpler, since this time pyruvic acid itself is the oxidizing agent, becoming reduced to **lactic acid**. The overall reaction is therefore:

$$CH_3COCOOH + NADH_2 \longrightarrow CH_3CH(OH)COOH + NAD$$

$$\text{pyruvic acid} \qquad\qquad\qquad\qquad \text{lactic acid}$$

As you see, the $C=O$ group of pyruvic acid has been reduced to $CH-OH$ by the two hydrogen atoms from $NADH_2$. The enzyme involved, present in the cytosol, is **lactate dehydrogenase**. (*In vivo*, lactic acid normally exists as lactate ions.) When exercise is over, the large amount of lactate accumulated as a result of anaerobic respiration by the muscles is oxidized back to pyruvate. This requires substantial amounts of oxygen—termed the **oxygen debt**—which is provided by the deep and rapid breathing that continues for some time after the period of physical activity.

6.5 REGULATION OF GLUCOSE CATABOLISM

When the bull charges and you run, both your muscles and his need a lot of ATP. Conversely, as sleep comes, very much less ATP is needed than in any daytime activity. How can the rate of catabolism be increased or decreased as required?

The question of biochemical regulation is a large and complex area of current interest. You have, however, already met the basic idea involved in one major method of control in ITQ 4 (Section 4.2). In that example, the theoretical idea introduced was that the product of a catabolic pathway might somehow alter the active site of an enzyme earlier in the pathway so that its activity would be decreased. The effective result of this would be that the build-up of product would 'switch off' the pathway that makes the product. This, obviously, would provide a method of regulating the build-up of product; it is very similar to the kind of control involved in a bathroom immersion heater—where the build-up of heat raises the temperature which, via the thermostat, switches off the heater. This kind of 'product switches off the process' method of control is described as control by **negative feedback**, and you will learn more about its applications to physiological systems in the next Unit.

Experiments have shown that just this kind of negative feedback system of control operates in most if not all biochemical pathways. Actual biochemical examples are somewhat more complicated than the simple immersion heater model: as well as a later product inhibiting an earlier enzyme (as in (a) below), it sometimes happens that an *earlier* metabolite *activates* a *later* enzyme. This idea is shown in (b) below.

(a) L $\longrightarrow$ M $\longrightarrow$ N $\longrightarrow$ O $\longrightarrow$ P $\longrightarrow$ Q

M-ase

a build-up of Q *inhibits* M-ase

(b) L $\longrightarrow$ M $\longrightarrow$ N $\longrightarrow$ O $\longrightarrow$ P $\longrightarrow$ Q

M-ase

a build-up of L *activates* M-ase

Enzymes such as M-ase, in our theoretical example above, that are subject to inhibition or activation by metabolites are called **regulatory enzymes**. One real example of an important regulatory enzyme is isocitrate dehydrogenase (ICDH, for short). As you can see from Figure 29 (p. 45), this enzyme catalyses the dehydrogenation of citric acid.

☐ Picture yourself inside the matrix of a mitochondrion. All around you are ATP molecules that have been produced by oxidative phosphorylation within the inner membrane nearby. Also, there are many ADP molecules on the way in to the phosphorylation process. There are also many molecules of the various TCA cycle enzymes close by, all of them sequentially engaged in catabolizing acetyl CoA molecules, with a consequent production of $NADH_2$ and $FADH_2$. Suppose the ATP concentration begins to get unnecessarily high (perhaps you've just ceased some energetic activity). To bring down the level of ATP and so achieve regulation, should TCA cycle activity increase or decrease?

■ Fairly obviously, it should decrease. By a similar argument, a rise in the concentration of ADP should lead to an *increase* in the rate of TCA cycle activity.

□ The activity of ICDH is relatively low, and it is the rate of the ICDH step that determines the activity of the whole TCA cycle. ICDH activity is affected by ATP and also by ADP. Do you think ATP activates or inhibits ICDH? What about the effect of ADP on ICDH?

■ ATP inhibits ICDH. ADP activates ICDH.

We shall not go into the mechanisms whereby metabolites such as ATP and ADP exert their effect on the activity of an enzyme such as ICDH. What you do know, however, is that the metabolite concerned binds to the enzyme and thereby alters its active site.

SUMMARY OF SECTION 6

1 Aerobic catabolism of glucose occurs in four stages: glycolysis, link reaction, tricarboxylic acid cycle and electron transport chain. The cellular locations of these are (respectively) cytosol, mitochondrial matrix, mitochondrial matrix and inner mitochondrial membrane.

2 Aerobic catabolism of glucose brings about (exactly) the overall reaction:

$$C_6H_{12}O_6 + 6O_2 \longrightarrow 6CO_2 + 6H_2O.$$

The chemical energy made available leads to the production of 38 ATP molecules and heat is produced as a by-product.

3 Glycolysis produces pyruvic acid and $NADH_2$. The link reaction converts pyruvic acid to acetyl CoA, carbon dioxide and more $NADH_2$. The TCA cycle converts acetyl CoA to carbon dioxide, more $NADH_2$ and some $FADH_2$. The electron transport chain uses oxygen to oxidize $NADH_2$ and $FADH_2$ to water, thereby regenerating NAD and FAD.

4 Substrate level phosphorylation (ATP synthesis not associated with the electron transport chain) yields 2 ATPs per molecule of glucose in glycolysis, and 2 ATPs per molecule of glucose via the TCA cycle.

5 Oxidative phosphorylation (ATP synthesis that is dependent on ETC activity) yields a total of 34 ATPs per molecule of glucose: 30 ATPs from the oxidation of 10 $NADH_2$ and 4 ATPs from the oxidation of 2 $FADH_2$.

6 As most of the ATP is made in mitochondria, these organelles are often known as the powerhouses of the cell.

7 Anaerobic catabolism occurs without oxygen. There is no ETC activity and, consequently, no TCA cycle or link reaction. Glycolysis continues because the product of glycolysis (pyruvic acid), directly or indirectly, is used to bring about the re-oxidation of $NADH_2$ produced by glycolysis to NAD. Ethanol and lactic acid are the end-products of anaerobic catabolism in yeast and muscle, respectively. ATP is produced entirely by substrate level phosphorylation.

8 The rate of catabolism is regulated in cells so that ATP production matches ATP needs. Regulation is achieved by increasing or decreasing the activity of certain regulatory enzymes.

SAQ 21 Which of the following statements about glucose catabolism are true?

(a) The link reaction occurs in the cytosol.

✓(b) Carbon dioxide is produced in glycolysis.

✓(c) Four molecules of reduced coenzymes are produced by each turn of the TCA cycle.

✓(d) A C_4 intermediate in the TCA cycle combines with pyruvic acid to give citric acid.

✓(e) The components of the electron transport chain are located in the inner mitochondrial membrane.

(f) One turn of the TCA cycle produces one molecule of carbon dioxide.

(g) The carbon dioxide breathed out by mammals has its origin in the link reaction and TCA cycle.

SAQ 22 Which of the following biochemical transformations involves: (a) CO_2 production; (b) $FADH_2$ production; (c) substrate level phosphorylation; (d) electron transport within the inner mitochondrial membrane?

d (i) $NADH_2 + \frac{1}{2}O_2 \longrightarrow NAD + H_2O$

    (ii) glucose $\longrightarrow$ pyruvic acid

a) (iii) glucose $\longrightarrow$ ethanol

b (iv) pyruvic acid $\longrightarrow$ acetyl CoA

D (v) acetyl CoA $\longrightarrow CO_2$

SAQ 23 The activity of the enzyme ICDH is affected by $NADH_2$ (as well as by ATP and ADP). Would you expect $NADH_2$ to be an activator or an inhibitor of ICDH? *Yes!*

7 CATABOLISM OF OTHER FUELS

Besides carbohydrates, most heterotrophs consume substantial amounts of fats and proteins. Equally, many plants make, store and catabolize proteins and fats in addition to starch. So we would expect to find effective biochemical systems for catabolizing such substances—as indeed there are.

Figure 27 (p. 43) implicitly promises there would be a 'pay-off' for mastering the scheme of glucose catabolism. The reward would be that the pathways of fat and protein catabolism would link in to what you already know. More precisely, we expect to find that the catabolism of glycerol, of long-chain fatty acids (together making fats: Section 3.2) and of each of 20 amino acids (derived from proteins), would give intermediate products that are components either of glycolysis or of the link reaction or of the TCA cycle. If this is the case, the end part of the catabolism of these other fuels will follow common routes; these routes (all three of them) are often called the **central pathways**.

Glycerol provides an instant and easy example. Once removed from a fat by hydrolysis, it is converted in the cytosol to another C_3 compound by two enzyme-catalysed reactions, as follows:

$$glycerol + ATP \longrightarrow \alpha\text{-glycerophosphate} + ADP$$

$$\alpha\text{-glycerophosphate} + NAD \longrightarrow dihydroxyacetone\ phosphate$$

$$+ NADH_2$$

You certainly do not need to remember these reactions. But a glance back at Figure 29 will show you that dihydroxyacetone phosphate is one of the intermediates of the glycolytic pathway. The route 'in' to the central pathways is, therefore, plain to see.

The catabolism of long-chain fatty acids, the other components of tri-glycerides, presents a more complex situation which we shall not explore in detail here. What happens is that the long fatty acid molecules are 'chopped up' into C_2 units. Look back to Table 1 (p. 15) to see the formulae of two very common fatty acids.

☐ How many carbon atoms are there in a molecule of palmitic acid, and of stearic acid? How many C_2 units could each of these fatty acids give? Can you suggest a likely identity for this C_2 unit?

■ Palmitic acid has 16 carbon atoms and stearic acid has 18. Thus the former will give eight C_2 units, and the latter, nine. The most obvious candidate for this C_2 unit is acetyl CoA (Figure 29).

In fact this is exactly what happens *in vivo*. A special set of enzymes forming another catabolic pathway, called the **β-oxidation pathway**, converts all such fatty acids to many molecules of acetyl CoA. These are then catabolized via the TCA cycle—acting, once again, in its capacity of a central pathway. The enzymes of the β-oxidation pathway are, like the TCA cycle enzymes, in solution in the mitochondrial matrix. This, of course, extends the 'power-house' role of the mitochondria.

Finally, what about the catabolism of amino acids? There are 20 of these and, indeed, there are 20 different 'beginnings' to their catabolic routes. However, we shall concentrate only on the general principles of amino acid catabolism. In all cases, this involves the removal of the nitrogen-containing amino group—and, not surprisingly, this process is called **deamination**. The non-nitrogenous acids remaining (different for each amino acid) are then catabolized further until they join into one or another of the central pathways. The amino group is removed by transfer to an acceptor molecule, and is ultimately excreted in a form which varies from organism to organism (ammonia in fish, urea in many mammals and uric acid in birds and reptiles).

ITQ 8   The following reaction shows the first stage in the catabolism of a particular amino acid in which the amino group is transferred to an acceptor molecule X. What is the name of the amino acid? What is the name of the residual carbon compound produced? In what way will the central pathways deal with this compound? (*Note:* The identity of X does not matter.)

$$CH_3CH(NH_2)COOH + X \longrightarrow CH_3COCOOH + XNH_2$$

In conclusion, the catabolism of all metabolic fuels (the food of hetero-trophs and the internally produced organic compounds of autotrophs) pro-ceeds ultimately via the central pathways that you met in glucose catabolism. These catabolic links are shown in outline terms in Figure 36.

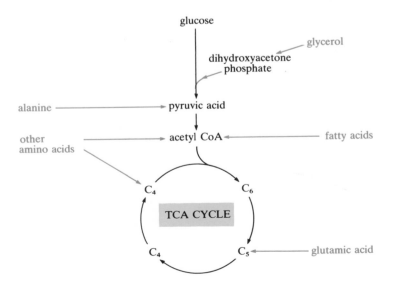

FIGURE 36   Catabolism of other substances besides glucose occurs via the central pathways. (The scheme shown here is much simplified.)

SUMMARY OF SECTION 7

1   Glycerol catabolism joins the glycolytic pathway.

2   Fatty acids are catabolized via the β-oxidation pathway to acetyl CoA, which is then catabolized via the TCA cycle.

3   The catabolism of different amino acids differs in detail. However, all are deaminated and the amino group is ultimately excreted, in one form or another. The residual carbon compound is catabolized via the central pathways; the products from different amino acids enter at different points.

4   With the major exception of the enzymes of the glycolytic pathway, the enzymes that catalyse catabolic reactions occur mainly within the matrix of mitochondria.

SAQ 24   How many ATPs are produced in the complete oxidation of the acetyl CoA molecules yielded by β-oxidation of palmitic acid? Do you think this likely to be the total amount of ATP that can be produced from palmitic acid?

8 THE SYNTHESIS OF CELLULAR COMPOUNDS

After so many pages about catabolism, we should remind ourselves of its role in the overall biochemical scheme. As you will recall from Sections 2 and 5, all organisms use the catabolically produced ATP in a variety of ways: the one of particular interest in this Section is its use in the range of *biosynthetic* processes that occur in cells. As well as providing ATP—the *energy* for biosynthesis—those same catabolic processes provide a whole range of *precursors*—the necessary chemical components for making things: if some biosynthesis or other requires a 'C$_2$ fragment', as does the synthesis of the steroid hormones in animals and vitamin A in plants, then not surprisingly acetyl CoA is the source.

There is one biosynthetic process, however, that stands apart from all others. And that, of course, is *photosynthesis*—the synthesis of carbohydrate in the cells of autotrophs, using carbon dioxide, water and light energy. This is the process on which almost all life, hence nearly all biochemistry, depends.

8.1 PHOTOSYNTHESIS

The overall reaction of photosynthesis can be represented in several ways. In the TV programme you will see this representation:

$$CO_2 + H_2O \xrightarrow{\text{solar energy}} [CH_2O] + O_2$$

This equation tells us that carbohydrate, [CH$_2$O], is formed from carbon dioxide and water using energy from the Sun. An alternative representation is:

$$6CO_2 + 6H_2O \xrightarrow{\text{solar energy}} C_6H_{12}O_6 + 6O_2$$

Both formulations have their advantages—but, overall, both remind us that in chemical terms we are looking at the exact reverse of glucose catabolism. Whereas in the latter glucose is oxidized and energy is liberated, in photosynthesis carbon dioxide is reduced, and this requires energy. The complementary nature of the processes of respiration and photosynthesis can be illustrated thus:

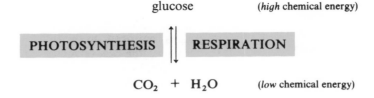

glucose   (*high* chemical energy)

PHOTOSYNTHESIS ‖ **RESPIRATION**

CO_2 + H_2O (*low* chemical energy)

The photosynthetic production of glucose has been shown to take place *in vivo*, in two distinct stages—a **light stage** in which ATP and a reduced coenzyme are made, and a subsequent **dark stage** in which these products of the light stage are *used* to convert carbon dioxide to carbohydrate. This chemical division of labour is matched by the physical arrangement within the chloroplast. Plate 6 shows a chloroplast of a leaf cell. The light stage occurs in the stacks of membranes that you can see clearly, and the reactions of the dark stage occur in the solution that fills the chloroplast between the membrane stacks. In Plate 7 you can see individual chloroplasts in the mesophyll cells of a leaf (these are the green cells that form the spongy interior of leaves). Figure 37 illustrates the relationship between light and dark stages of photosynthesis.

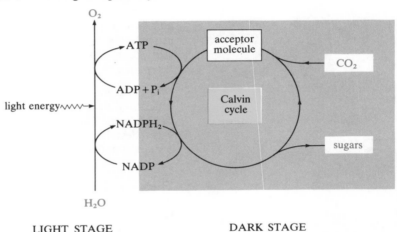

LIGHT STAGE   DARK STAGE

FIGURE 37   The relationship between the light and dark stages of photosynthesis. These occur, respectively, in the chloroplast membranes and in the solution within the chloroplast. (For simplicity, none of the intermediates of the Calvin cycle are shown or named.)

In the light stage, light energy is trapped by the green pigment chlorophyll and then used to convert ADP and P_i to ATP and to bring about the reduction of the coenzyme **NADP** to $NADPH_2$ (different from NAD: see Table 4, p. 31) by using the hydrogen atoms in water. If you look at the overall equation for the latter process, it is plain that much energy is needed, for it is, effectively, the reverse of the events in the electron transport chain. The equation is:

$$NADP + H_2O \longrightarrow NADPH_2 + \tfrac{1}{2}O_2$$

ITQ 9   Remembering the technique of isotopic labelling, how could you use the isotope ^{18}O (the usual isotope of oxygen is ^{16}O) to check whether photosynthetically produced oxygen originates from water molecules, as implied by this equation?

The light energy that brings about the formation of ATP during photosynthesis (a process called **photophosphorylation**) and of $NADPH_2$ has its effect through a number of very complicated and still incompletely understood mechanisms. Essentially, these involve absorption of light by certain kinds of chlorophyll molecule, the subsequent excitation of electrons in the mol-

CALVIN CYCLE

STOMATA

ecules of chlorophyll (rather in the manner you saw in Units 11–12) followed, ultimately, by the emission of electrons that bring about the reduction of NADP to $NADPH_2$ and the conversion of ADP + P_i to ATP.

If the light stage is complicated, so also is the dark stage! The sequence of steps that occur in the watery non-membranous regions of the chloroplasts involves the conversion of carbon dioxide, by a cyclic sequence of reactions, to carbohydrate. This cycle of reactions is called the **Calvin cycle**, after its principal discoverer. These conversions have been followed by isotopic labelling methods using $^{14}CO_2$. The carbon dioxide necessary for photosynthesis enters leaves via small pores in the leaf epidermis (the 'skin' of the leaf) that can open and close as needed. These pores are called **stomata** (singular stoma), and are shown in Figure 38 and Plate 8.

8.2 OTHER BIOSYNTHETIC ROUTES

The account of photosynthesis given above covers only part of the essential biosynthetic power of plants. As well as making carbohydrates, plants synthesize all other organic compounds from inorganic sources. Water reaching the leaves from the roots carries sulphate ions and nitrate ions in solution. A comparison of the formulae of these ions (SO_4^{2-} and NO_3^-) with that of a typical nitrogen- and sulphur-containing metabolite, for example the amino acid cysteine (Table 3), shows that chemical *reduction* is an essential part of the conversion. Once formed, these simpler compounds provide plants with the precursors for all other biosyntheses. Remember that plants are entirely self-sufficient in terms of organic molecules—unlike heterotrophs, where what cannot be made must be supplied in the diet.

All organisms however—plants, animals and bacteria—have a biosynthetic capacity that makes the best of our laboratory-based efforts look feeble by comparison. The recipe, as you now know well, involves ATP produced in ways described earlier, precursors of every type available in the highly ordered interior of cells, and enzymes of an activity determined by the cellular environment.

The kind of biosynthesis involved can be pictured if you think of a bacterium growing in a simple solution of glucose, phosphate ions and one or two amino acids as its source of nitrogen and sulphur. Somehow within the cell, intermediates in the catabolism of glucose and the amino acids have to be drawn off and reassembled to give, for example, the complex polysaccharides of the bacterial cell wall, the proteins and phospholipids of the cell membrane, the thousand or so different proteins constituting the enzymic apparatus of the cell, the DNA of the chromosome, the RNA, and the small but complex coenzymes that work with the enzymes. In larger organisms, ourselves for example, the characterless soup of amino acids, sugars, fatty acids and glycerol that are taken across the intestinal wall and catabolized, have also to provide the intermediates for a set of precise cellular molecules even more diverse than those of the bacterium.

And, to return to where we began, it is on a well ordered system of cell biochemistry, involving an adjustable balance of interrelated catabolism and anabolism, that growth and survival depend. Well-being at the cellular level depends in its turn, however, on harmony between the different tissues, organs and organ systems, and also on an efficient relationship with the external environment. In both these respects—internal balance and communication with the environment—cell chemistry depends on physiology. And it is to this level of organization that we look in the next Unit.

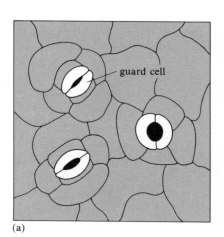

(a)

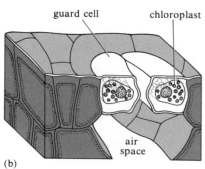

(b)

FIGURE 38 (a) View of a leaf surface showing three stomata. (b) A stoma that has been cut through and is viewed from the side. The chloroplasts can be seen in the guard cells that surround the stoma. (Guard cells can change in size and so alter the size of the stoma.)

SUMMARY OF SECTION 8

1   The most fundamental biosynthetic process is photosynthesis. Virtually all life depends on compounds made in this way.

2   In green plants, photosynthesis occurs in chloroplasts. In overall terms it is the reverse of respiration.

3 The process is divided between light stage and dark stage. The former occurs in the membranes of chloroplasts and generates ATP and $NADPH_2$. The latter occurs in the solution between chloroplast membranes. Here, ATP and $NADPH_2$ are used to convert carbon dioxide (obtained from the exterior via stomata) to carbohydrate. The pathway involves a cycle of reactions called the Calvin cycle.

4 Plants are able to synthesize other compounds from inorganic sources: for example, nitrate ions and sulphate ions are converted to organic nitrogen- and sulphur-containing compounds.

5 All organisms have a remarkable biosynthetic capacity. This depends, as always, on a supply of ATP, on a supply of precursor substances and on the metabolic organization provided by specific enzymes of controllable activity.

6 Anabolism and catabolism are both essential for growth and survival. Organization at the physiological level is also important.

SAQ 25 In what ways are the processes of photophosphorylation and oxidative phosphorylation apparently similar?

SAQ 26 Using a suitable disruptive technique, chloroplasts from spinach were broken open and then separated into membranous and soluble components, labelled A and B respectively. Both were found to be biochemically active. Which of the following properties belonged to which component(s)?

(i)   contained chlorophyll;
(ii) converted $^{14}CO_2$ to $^{14}C_6H_{12}O_6$;
(iii) produced $^{18}O_2$ from $H_2{}^{18}O$.

SAQ 27 Which of the following statements about biosynthesis are true?

(a) Biosynthetic pathways involve the conversion of ATP to $ADP + P_i$.

(b) All ATP produced in catabolism is used in anabolism.

(c) Some catabolic pathways are involved in ATP production whereas different catabolic pathways are involved in precursor production.

(d) Heterotrophs are able to synthesize all the coenzymes they require, provided the necessary vitamins are supplied in the diet.

9 TV NOTES: THE FIRES OF LIFE

The programme is mainly concerned with putting biochemistry in the context of biology as a whole. As much of it deals with principles rather than details, you can usefully view it without studying the text. However, there is a close relationship between text and TV and these notes highlight the points you should at least skim through before seeing the programme.

The programme begins by looking at autotrophs and heterotrophs and goes on to examine how energy, made available by glucose oxidation, is used within organisms. Sections 2.2 and 2.3 are especially relevant to this part of the programme.

The middle part of the programme examines the oxidative process more closely, dealing with the metabolic roles of the various parts of the cell. You should remind yourself about the components of cells, by reading Section 5.2. Some experimental detail is included in the programme, and the discussion of centrifugation and of the measurement of respiration rates (also in Section 5.2) is helpful here.

Later in the programme, we refer to the electron transport chain. This is introduced in Section 6.1, and developed in Section 6.3. The diagram of the ETC shown in the programme is a simplification of Figure 33.

As noted above, the aim of the programme is to provide a 'feel' for the relevance of biochemistry to biology; to show that the living world, of organisms and populations of organisms, relates directly to the chemical events in cells. To this end, most of the programme is set out-of-doors or in temporary laboratories. Much of the essential sophistication of the normal research laboratory is necessarily out of sight. With this cautionary note at the back of your mind, attention can be paid to the main aim of the programme, which is to show that solar energy ultimately drives all the processes of life. Whatever the intermediate energy conversions, that input of solar energy eventually appears as heat: the law of conservation of energy applies in biology as in all energy-converting systems.

OBJECTIVES FOR UNIT 22

After you have worked through this Unit you should be able to:

1   Explain the meaning of, and use correctly, all the terms flagged in the text. (*SAQs 9–13 and 16*)

2   Relate the parts played by DNA, chemical energy and precursor substances to growth. (*ITQs 2 and 7, SAQs 5 and 6*)

3   Compare and contrast the biochemical features of autotrophs and heterotrophs. (*ITQ 1, SAQs 1, 2, 3 and 4*)

4   Solve problems and recognize descriptions relating to the structure and function of metabolites, precursors, fats, polysaccharides and proteins. (*ITQ 3, SAQs 8, 12, 14 and 15*)

5   Assess statements about the role of ATP and ADP, and also about heat production, and calculate amounts of ATP produced. (*SAQs 7 and 24*)

6   Relate the properties of enzymes regarding catalysis, specificity, temperature and pH response, substrate and coenzyme binding, to higher-order structure of proteins and hence to enzyme active sites and activity. (*ITQ 5, SAQs 17, 18 and 19*)

7   Design simple experiments and solve problems concerning the assay of enzymes. (*Experiment*)

8   Comment on and solve problems about methods of biochemical investigation. (*ITQ 6, SAQ 20*)

9   Assign biochemical functions to various parts of animal and plant cells. (*SAQ 26*)

10   Relate the component parts of glucose catabolism to the whole. (*SAQs 21 and 22*)

11   Recognize the effects on biochemical systems of the absence of oxygen. (*SAQ 22*)

12   Recognize warranted, unwarranted, plausible and implausible statements about metabolic regulation. (*ITQ 4, SAQ 23*)

13   Relate the catabolism of fuels other than glucose to common routes of catabolism in the central pathways. (*ITQ 8, SAQ 24*)

14   Relate the light and dark stages to the overall process of photosynthesis. (*ITQ 9, SAQs 25 and 26*)

15   Relate anabolism and catabolism. (*SAQ 27*)

ITQ ANSWERS AND COMMENTS

ITQ 1 From everyday experience, you know that green plants require light. Plants convert light energy into chemical energy (in the carbohydrates they make by photosynthesis). The nitrogen atoms of plant proteins and nucleic acids come mainly from nitrate ions (NO_3^-) in the soil: similarly sulphur, required in certain amino acids, comes from the sulphate (SO_4^{2-}) in the soil. Gardeners will be familiar with the practice of adding nitrates and sulphates. Ammonium salts, also supplied as fertilizers, are converted to nitrates in soil (though plants can absorb some of their nitrogen as ammonium ions directly). The importance of also providing plants with phosphate ions will be clear when you have read Section 2.3.

ITQ 2 The processes or activities that involve energy expenditure are: anabolism (biosynthesis); movement of the organism; movement of substances from a region of low to a region of high concentration; and production of light. In all these energy conversions heat is also produced.

ITQ 3 The equation for the reaction is given below. Note that, because three hydroxyl groups condense with three carboxyl groups, three molecules of water are formed per molecule of fat synthesized.

$$
\begin{array}{ll}
CH_2-OH & CH_3-(CH_2)_{14}-\overset{\displaystyle O}{\underset{\displaystyle \|}{C}}-OH \\
CH-OH \quad + & CH_3-(CH_2)_{14}-\overset{\displaystyle O}{\underset{\displaystyle \|}{C}}-OH \rightleftharpoons \\
CH_2-OH & CH_3-(CH_2)_{14}-\overset{\displaystyle O}{\underset{\displaystyle \|}{C}}-OH
\end{array}
$$

glycerol   palmitic acid

$$
\begin{array}{l}
CH_2-O-\overset{\displaystyle O}{\underset{\displaystyle \|}{C}}-(CH_2)_{14}-CH_3 \\
CH-O-\overset{\displaystyle O}{\underset{\displaystyle \|}{C}}-(CH_2)_{14}-CH_3 + 3H_2O \\
CH_2-O-\overset{\displaystyle O}{\underset{\displaystyle \|}{C}}-(CH_2)_{14}-CH_3
\end{array}
$$

glyceryl tripalmitate

ITQ 4 If the active site is somehow 'distorted' so that it no longer fits the substrate molecule as well, less enzyme–substrate complex will be formed and the rate of catalysis will be less. If effective regulation of metabolism requires that flow of metabolites along pathway A $\longrightarrow$ B $\longrightarrow$ C $\longrightarrow$ D be reduced, a rate-diminishing alteration in the active site of A-ase might be brought about by (say) the presence of D, as illustrated in the diagram.

inhibiting effect of metabolite
D on the enzyme A-ase

As you will see in Section 6.5, this is in fact one of the ways in which enzyme activity is actually regulated.

ITQ 5 A decrease in pH means an increase in H^+ concentration. If this happens, ionized carboxyl groups tend to become unionized, viz:

$$
R-\overset{\displaystyle O}{\underset{\displaystyle \|}{C}}-O^- + H^+ \rightleftharpoons R-\overset{\displaystyle O}{\underset{\displaystyle \|}{C}}-OH
$$

Conversely, an increase in pH means a decrease in H^+ concentration, which shifts the above equilibrium to the left.

As higher-order structure (hence the shape of the active site) depends on ionic interactions between the R groups of amino acid residues in proteins, it follows that changes in pH will affect enzyme activity.

ITQ 6 You would expect to find ^{14}C in all the intermediates A, B and C, and in pyruvic acid. You would predict that ^{14}C would appear first in A, then B, then C and then pyruvic acid (thus providing evidence that this is the actual order of the intermediates in the pathway).

ITQ 7 (a) About 1 860 kJ; (b) 38%.

(a) As 38 moles of ATP are made, $38 \times 30\,kJ = 1\,140$ kJ of the chemical energy of glucose are converted into this form. We know that 3 000 kJ are made available in the complete oxidation of one mole of glucose, so $(3\,000 - 1\,140)\,kJ = 1\,860\,kJ$ are liberated as heat.

(b) The percentage of the chemical energy in glucose that is converted into the chemical energy of ATP is $(1\,140/3\,000) \times 100\% = 38\%$.

ITQ 8 The amino acid is alanine. The product is pyruvic acid. This is catabolized via the link reaction, the TCA cycle and the electron transport chain.

ITQ 9 $H_2{}^{18}O$ could be supplied and the evolved oxygen could be examined for $^{18}O_2$. This experiment, first done in 1941, showed that the oxygen produced by photosynthesis comes exclusively from water.

SAQ ANSWERS AND COMMENTS

SAQ 1   During the hour, two processes occur: respiration and photosynthesis. The first produces carbon dioxide and uses oxygen, the second uses carbon dioxide (and water from the soil) and produces oxygen. In bright sunlight, photosynthesis predominates. Therefore, you would find an overall increase in oxygen concentration and decrease in carbon dioxide concentration. However, during winter, or in the shade, there would be a lower rate of photosynthesis and the rate of the two processes may be equal, so that there would be no change in the relative proportions of oxygen and carbon dioxide.

SAQ 2   This time there would be no photosynthesis but respiration would continue. Oxygen concentration would fall and carbon dioxide concentration would rise.

SAQ 3   Some source of nitrogen, sulphur, and phosphorus must be provided. As a heterotroph, *E. coli* can use amino acids for N and S (and phosphate for P). Unlike most heterotrophs, however, it can also use inorganic sources of the elements N and S.

SAQ 4   Oxygen concentration would fall and carbon dioxide concentration would rise, due to respiration of the bacterial cells.

SAQ 5   The labelled glucose would be catabolized to provide energy *and precursors*. These precursors would be used in many biosyntheses. For example, polysaccharides (in the bacterial cell wall) and fats will contain the ^{14}C label. Labelled carbon will also make its way into nucleotides (hence DNA and RNA) and amino acids (hence proteins). In fact all the organic components of the *E. coli* cells will eventually become labelled with ^{14}C.

SAQ 6   The different catabolic powers of the two strains are due to differences in their enzymic machinery. The second strain has enzymes that can deal with fructose but not glucose. As noted in the question, the trait is inherited: the two strains of *E. coli* differ in their genes. As you know (Section 2.1) different genes bring about the formation of different proteins, in this case enzyme proteins.

SAQ 7   (a) No change; (b) increases; (c) increases.

(a) Although ATP levels will remain roughly constant, there will be a greater rate of ATP synthesis and breakdown (turnover), as the ADP/ATP system links the high energy *demands* of your working muscles with the high energy *output* of rapid glucose oxidation in your muscle cells.

(b) Glucose oxidation (cell respiration) requires oxygen and also produces an equivalent amount of carbon dioxide that is ultimately eliminated via the lungs. Respiration rate increases so carbon dioxide output increases too.

(c) Heat is produced when ATP is made and used (Figure 8). Since the rate of turnover of ATP increases, heat output will also increase.

SAQ 8   X (ii); Y (iii) and (vi); Z (i).

X: Alanine is an amino acid (Table 1); amino acids are precursors of proteins and haemoglobin is a protein.

Y: Palmitic acid is a fatty acid; fatty acids and glycerol are the precursors of fats.

Z: Glucose is the precursor of the polysaccharide glycogen.

SAQ 9   Lipase catalyses the hydrolysis of fats to glycerol and long-chain fatty acids such as palmitic acid and stearic acid. These are weak acids, partially dissociating in solution to give hydrogen ions. For example, palmitic acid ionizes to produce palmitate and H^+ ions:

$$CH_3-(CH_2)_{14}-\underset{\underset{O}{\|}}{C}-OH \rightleftharpoons CH_3-(CH_2)_{14}-\underset{\underset{O}{\|}}{C}-O^- + H^+$$

palmitic acid   palmitate

Thus hydrogen ion concentration increases so pH decreases.

SAQ 10   The ester formed is called a mixed triglyceride ('mixed' because it contains more than one kind of long-chain fatty acid). One possible formula is:

The other possible structure would have a different order of fatty acid residues: stearic, palmitic, stearic; instead of stearic, stearic, palmitic (as shown above).

SAQ 11   Four water molecules are produced, one for each of the four glycosidic bonds within the pentasaccharide.

SAQ 12   (a) Cellulose (see Table 1); (b) hydrolysis occurs at the β-1,4 glycosidic bonds (see Figure 11); (c) the enzyme that catalyses the hydrolysis of cellulose is cellulase.

SAQ 13   A: isomaltose; B: maltose; C: cellobiose.

You can see that the compound A contains an α-1,6 glycosidic bond and must therefore have come only from the branched polysaccharide, glycogen; so A must be isomaltose.

B contains an α-1,4 glycosidic bond, so you would expect it to have come from amylose and the non-branching parts of glycogen; the disaccharide obtained from *both* amylose *and* glycogen is maltose.

C contains a β-1,4 glycosidic bond, so must be the product of cellulose hydrolysis.

(Note that, for all three polysaccharides, the ultimate product of hydrolysis is the monosaccharide glucose.)

SAQ 14 (a) True. Proteins are polymers of amino acids, so they all yield amino acids on hydrolysis.

(b) False. A given protein may not contain all 20 kinds of amino acid.

(c) False. When 100 amino acids condense, the polypeptide thus formed has 100 residues joined by 99 peptide bonds.

(d) False. The mutation may alter a residue in the sequence which does *not* contribute to higher-order structure.

SAQ 15 A circular polypeptide would be formed. These actually exist in nature.

SAQ 16 A *protein* is the whole, functional (i.e. biologically active) molecule. Some proteins of this type indeed contain but a single polypeptide chain, for example, myoglobin. Others, however, have two or more polypeptide chains in one functional molecule. Examples are insulin, with two chains in one molecule, covalently linked; and haemoglobin, with four chains in one molecule, held together by weak bonds.

SAQ 17 (a) Hydrogen atoms are transferred from BH_2 (and JH_2) to NAD; $NADH_2$ is formed as a result. (b) The enzyme involved—we could call it 'BH_2 dehydrogenase'—has an active site tailored to bind BH_2 and NAD. Presumably, it is able to bind JH_2 less well because the 'lock and key' fit is less good. This kind of explanation accounts for the marked specificity of the enzyme for BH_2.

SAQ 18 (a) As its name suggests, the protease is a protein-digesting enzyme. It hydrolyses peptide bonds in proteins eaten by the mammal. (b) The enzyme works best at pH 8, so it is likely that the higher-order structure at pH 8 provides an effective active site. At pH 2, the higher-order structure is likely to be different. As a consequence the active site would probably be changed and so the activity would probably be lower.

SAQ 19 If the pH of both blood samples were the same, you could safely say that sample A has three times the concentration of enzyme Z as sample B. This is because rate is proportional to enzyme concentration, if the conditions are the same. As the pH of the two blood samples differs, a quantitative comparison cannot be made. However, as the pH values are close (7.2 and 7.4), it is probable that sample A contains a substantially greater concentration of Z than sample B. If, however, the activity against pH curve were very steep on both sides of the optimum, the small pH difference *might* account for much of the activity difference!

SAQ 20 Only (i) is expected. The homogenate contains both cytosol and mitochondria and oxygen, so the oxidation can proceed to completion. (ii) is not possible because oxygen is absent. (iii) does not occur because mitochondria can catabolize pyruvic acid but not glucose.

SAQ 21 (c), (e) and (g) are true; (a), (b), (d) and (f) are false.

(a) The link reaction occurs in the mitochondrial matrix.

(b) No carbon dioxide is produced in glycolysis: glucose (C_6) is converted to pyruvate (two C_3 molecules), and no carbon atoms are lost.

(c) $3NADH_2 + FADH_2$, so four molecules altogether.

(d) The C_4 intermediate combines with *acetyl CoA* (C_2) to give citric acid (C_6).

(e) The location of the carriers in the electron transport chain is illustrated in Frame 12 of the AV sequence and in Figure 34a.

(f) *Two* carbon dioxide molecules are produced in one turn of the TCA cycle.

(g) All the carbon dioxide is produced in the link reaction and the TCA cycle taking place within the mitochondria.

SAQ 22 (i): (d); (ii): (c) and, indirectly, (d); (iii): (a) and (c); (iv): (a) and, indirectly, (d); (v): (a), (b), (c) and (d).

Note: In (ii) $NADH_2$ must be reoxidized to NAD by the ETC, otherwise the product would be lactic acid not pyruvic acid. Hence, indirectly, electron transport activity must be involved.

SAQ 23 The more TCA cycle activity there is, the more $NADH_2$ is produced. If $NADH_2$ concentration rises, then (for regulation) TCA cycle activity must diminish. Therefore $NADH_2$ should inhibit ICDH activity.

SAQ 24 Palmitic acid, $CH_3(CH_2)_{14}COOH$, gives 8 acetyl CoA molecules. Each one of these gives 12 ATP molecules. This is because each produces $3NADH_2$ (9 ATPs) and $1FADH_2$ (2 ATPs) i.e. 11 ATPs by oxidative phosphorylation, plus 1ATP by substrate level phosphorylation in the TCA cycle. Thus, there are $8 \times 12 = 96$ ATPs produced. If you compare the formula of the acetyl group (CH_3CO) in acetyl CoA with the more highly reduced CH_2CH_2 from which it originates in the fatty acid, you will appreciate that still more reduced coenzymes would be produced by complete oxidation of palmitic acid. Thus the ATP yield is actually higher than the 96 molecules calculated above.

SAQ 25 They both involve making ATP from ADP $+ P_i$, and both occur in membrane-bound organelles with a membranous interior. Both depend on a flow of electrons.

SAQ 26 (i) A; (ii) B; (iii) A.

A, consisting of the chloroplast membranes, contains all the components necessary for the *light stage*. Only B, consisting of the solution between the chloroplast membranes, contains the enyzmes of the *dark stage*.

SAQ 27 (a) and (d) are true; (b) and (c) are false.

Regarding (b), ATP is used in many other processes (see Section 2). Regarding (c), the central pathways produce both ATP *and* precursors.

INDEX FOR UNIT 22

ACKNOWLEDGEMENTS

Grateful acknowledgement is made to the following for permission to reproduce material in this Unit:

Plate 1 from M. F. Perutz, *The Hemoglobin Molecule*, copyright © 1964 by Scientific American, Inc., all rights reserved; *Plate 2* after M. F. Perutz *The Hemoglobin Molecule*, copyright © 1964 by Scientific American, Inc., all rights reserved; *Plate 4* from E. Brachet, and H. E. Mirskey *The Cell*, 2nd edn, 1961, © Academic Press; *Plate 5* from *Journal of Ultrastructure Research*, supp. 4, p. 37, 1984, © Academic Press.

THE OPEN UNIVERSITY
A SCIENCE FOUNDATION COURSE

UNIT 23 PHYSIOLOGY

STUDY GUIDE

This Unit consists of a main text and TV programme. There is one experiment (in Section 3) that should take you about 45 minutes to complete. It involves taking mild exercise (stepping on and off a step about 100 times) and measuring your pulse. No special equipment is needed—but if, for any reason, it would be unwise for you to exercise in this way, you should look for someone to act as your subject.

The TV programme shows a number of physiological measurements being made, and the experiments that you will see tie in directly with the text, notably Section 5 on glucose supply. It is not essential for you to read the text before seeing the programme, but you should read the TV notes at the beginning of the Introduction.

The Unit follows closely on from Unit 22, dealing with the way in which physiological processes provide cells with oxygen and glucose for catabolism and remove from them the products of catabolism. Although many of the detailed examples come from *human* physiology, you should pay attention to the references to other animals whose physiology is different. As well as making these physiological comparisons, the Unit refers often to the evolutionarily important theme of the relationship of structure to function: you should be aware of these (necessarily) scattered references. A further important theme of the Unit is that of physiological regulation and control. The main development of this topic is in Section 6.

I INTRODUCTION AND TV PROGRAMME

In the TV programme 'A day in the life' you will see how physiological measurements are made. You already know something about physiological measurements from the TV programme 'Practically speaking', associated with Unit 4, and you will be measuring heart rate during your study of Unit 23. 'A day in the life' follows on from the previous programme on chemical energy, 'The fires of life', and looks at the whole organism. Measurements will be made on humans, and you should note the techniques that are used.

The programme centres on the link between food intake (type, calorific value, etc.) and energy supply for movement. The calorific value of food is measured by using a bomb calorimeter. A sample of food is completely oxidized inside a metal 'bomb', which absorbs the heat produced. From the rise in temperature of the 'bomb', the heat produced by the oxidation can be calculated.

The physiological measurements will be made on a man during his normal working day. He will be taking some exercise while the experiment is in progress. Unit 4 introduced you to the idea of control experiments, and a control will be used here. The measurements made on Sam, the exercising volunteer, will be compared with the values obtained from the sedentary narrator who will constitute the control. Both will be fed a standard meal, whose calorific value has been measured, and we will 'watch' the movement of glucose into the blood by taking blood samples at intervals. We shall monitor heart rate and measure respiration rate. You should ensure that you can make notes about the values obtained from the measurements.

Your aim is to be able to describe:

(a) how energy is derived from food;
(b) how blood glucose levels vary during the day;
(c) how the circulatory system performance is matched to demand;
(d) what the limits on human performance are.

PHYSIOLOGY

In Unit 22 you were introduced to the biochemical processes that generate usable energy, in the form of ATP, by breaking down carbohydrates and other compounds in a controlled manner. As most of these cellular reactions are overall oxidations, we need to ask: how do organisms obtain oxygen from their environment and convey it to the mitochondria deep within the cells? A similar question should be asked about the nutrients: how is what a lion eats, or what a plant makes in its leaves, delivered in the correct chemical form to the catabolic enzymes of the energy-requiring cells? Turning to the products of catabolism, the ATP that is formed is rapidly reconverted to ADP and P_i as it is used in cellular reactions. But what of the 'waste products'—water, heat, carbon dioxide and, if amino acids are the fuel, the various compounds of nitrogen—how are they removed from the organism? In addition to the relatively simple questions of reactants and products, there is the product of *regulation* and *co-ordination*. Sleeping and running pose very different demands in terms of the supply of fuel and oxygen and the disposal of waste. How is each of these controlled? The Unit deals with these questions, sometimes very briefly and sometimes in detail. In so doing, it ranges from looking at small simple animals to considering the lungs, heart and kidneys of larger ones.

The study of function in living organisms is called **physiology**, a word that comes from the Greek meaning 'knowledge of natural things'. This term has been in use for about 200 years but, as the study of nature has broadened in the 20th century, physiology has become restricted in meaning. It may now be defined informally as the study of how animals and plants work. You will see shortly that physiology makes considerable use of physics and, in particular, classical mechanics to account for what is observed in living systems. This should not be very surprising since you known by now that there is no need to invoke a separate unique 'vital force' to distinguish between what is inert and what is alive. One can wonder at the diversity and complexity of nature, but nature must conform to the same physical laws as everything else in the Universe. Let us apply this kind of approach to the 'supply and disposal' problems noted above—beginning with oxygen.

2 OXYGEN SUPPLY

In Unit 22, Section 2.3 you were introduced to the idea that almost all organisms depend on oxidative reactions to provide them with usable energy in the form of ATP. Heterotrophs oxidize food they have eaten; autotrophs oxidize the organic compounds that they have made for themselves—usually by photosynthesis. The overall equation for this oxidation is:

$$C_6H_{12}O_6 + 6O_2 \longrightarrow 6CO_2 + 6H_2O + \text{energy} \qquad (1)$$

How is oxygen 'captured' from the environment and delivered to the mitochondria in the right quantities to sustain this reaction?

2.1 DIFFUSION OF OXYGEN MOLECULES

As you might expect, the way in which oxygen is delivered to cells varies from one organism to another—fish are different from worms, and single-celled organisms are different from locusts, which in turn are different from humans. However, there is a common starting point—the oxygen in the Earth's atmosphere. The layer of air seven miles deep, dense at ground level and progressively thinner as altitude increases, contains about 20% of oxygen by volume; the rest is mainly nitrogen. This means that at sea-level in one litre of air there is about 200 cm^3 of oxygen—a concentration of $200 \text{ cm}^3 \text{l}^{-1}$. In biological terms, this is a rich source of supply: around 5 m^3 of air will provide enough oxygen molecules to catabolize all the food you eat in a day. Where the supply problem arises, however, is in the extraction of oxygen from the air and the delivery of it to the cells that need it.

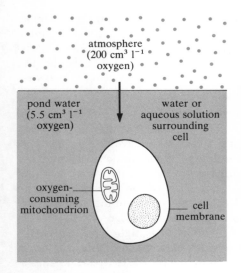

FIGURE 1 Oxygen capture from a gaseous mixture and transport to a solution within a single-celled organism.

The mechanisms for oxygen capture and transport that have evolved are many and varied, but there are underlying features common to all organisms: all involve the movement of gaseous oxygen molecules from the air, via a solution outside the cells to solution in the cytosol within the cells. With this kind of route, which is illustrated for a single-celled organism in Figure 1, various physical difficulties have had to be overcome in the course of evolution—and chief among these is the relative insolubility of oxygen in aqueous solution.

For aquatic organisms, the significance of solubility is plain. Although the atmosphere contains a high concentration of oxygen (about $200 \, cm^3 \, l^{-1}$), the oxygen content of natural waters is very much less, varying from almost zero in stagnant waters to a maximum of about $10 \, cm^3 \, l^{-1}$.

> Using your general knowledge of rivers and seas around the world, what do you think could account for such variation?

One factor is temperature. As the temperature rises, so the amount of gas in solution falls: at 30 °C freshwater only contains $5.5 \, cm^3 \, l^{-1}$ oxygen, whereas at 0 °C it contains almost twice as much. Thus the cold waters of the Arctic are comparatively rich in oxygen and, partly for this reason, contain a large quantity of organisms. The solubility of oxygen is also influenced by the amounts of other solutes present: salts in solution reduce the concentration of oxygen dissolved in seawater to about three-quarters of that present in freshwater at the same temperature. Pressure also has a marked effect: at high altitudes, where atmospheric pressure is low, the concentration of dissolved oxygen is also lower than it would be at sea-level.

But, whatever the nature of an organism's environment, a significant part of the route travelled by the oxygen molecules as they journey from environment to mitochondria will be in solution, as you have seen in Figure 1. This is as true for terrestrial animals as for aquatic ones and, indeed, is also true for plants.

In any solution, the molecules of solute and solvent (Units 13–14, Section 6.1) are in continuous motion. The motion is random, with frequent collisions between molecules. If coloured solute molecules are used, such as those of red ink in Figure 2, you can see that the solute molecules migrate from regions of high solute concentration to regions of lower solute concentration. If left until a stable state is reached, the solute concentration would

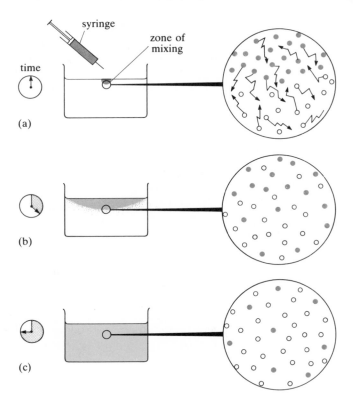

FIGURE 2 An example of diffusion. When a droplet of ink falls on to the surface of water in a container, the ink gradually disperses throughout the water. This is the result of the random movement of molecules (shown by the arrows in (a)). Water molecules gradually pervade the ink drop, and (over time) ink molecules spread out into the water ((b) and (c)).

• ink molecules
o water molecules

DIFFUSION

CONCENTRATION GRADIENT

EXTRACELLULAR FLUID

be the same in all parts of the solution—in Figure 2, for example, a pale pink solution of ink molecules throughout. This passive movement of small molecules from a zone of high concentration to one of low concentration is called **diffusion**—and the greater the **concentration gradient** (that is, the difference between the two concentrations divided by the distance between them), the greater is the rate of diffusion.

This has important consequences for oxygen transport, as you can see by looking again at Figure 1. Here the solute and solvent are, respectively, oxygen and water. When the cell respires and mitochondria use oxygen, the concentration of oxygen in the cytosol near each mitochondrion falls. Oxygen molecules diffuse into those zones from other parts of the cytosol, and—in like manner—the oxygen in those parts of the cytosol is replenished by diffusion of oxygen across the cell membrane from the fluid outside the cell (**extracellular fluid**). When mitochondria are active and use much oxygen, the rate at which it is replaced by diffusion is high; when activity is lower, the rate of diffusion is slower. In the ink example in Figure 2, a stable state is eventually reached. Continuous mitochondrial activity means that a stable state—an even concentration of oxygen—never occurs in the cell.

This description of oxygen diffusion into cells is almost the complete story of oxygen supply for unicellular organisms. A single cell needs only a small amount of oxygen, in absolute terms, and the distance the oxygen has to travel is small. Oxygen enters the cell through the membrane fast enough to provide oxygen for all the oxidative reactions. In organisms made up of many cells, the distance over which the oxygen must diffuse is potentially greater. As you will see, the problem is solved in different ways.

2.2 OXYGEN SUPPLY IN SMALL MULTICELLULAR ORGANISMS

Imagine now a small multicellular organism consisting of a lump or a few layers of cells. Because of increasing distances from the oxygen-containing outside environment to oxygen-requiring mitochondria, the concentration gradients involved become much lower. You can see this clearly in Figure 3: here the oxygen concentration at the margin is C_1 and that at the core of the lump is C_2, and the distance between the two is d, giving a concentration gradient of $(C_1 - C_2)$ divided by d. Hence, in a mass of cells of this type oxygen demand would be *high* because there are many cells, yet the rate of oxygen transport by diffusion would be *low* because of the low concentration gradient brought about by the relatively great distance from outside to cells. Such a situation of high demand and inadequate supply would be most unsatisfactory for the organism, and it is not surprising that a situation of the type described in Figure 3 does not occur in nature. In fact, layers of cells in any organism *are never more than about a millimetre from the nearest oxygen-rich extracellular solution*—and, as you will see, this 'less than a millimetre' rule applies both to cells concerned with the acquisition of oxygen (in the lungs, for example) and to those that consume oxygen deep within tissues. You will find that this 'rule'—arising, as you might guess, from the extreme slowness with which oxygen molecules are able to diffuse through water—is of great biological importance and will be referred to often in the following text.

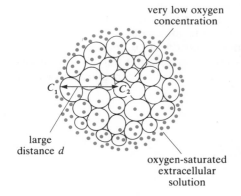

very low oxygen concentration

large distance d

oxygen-saturated extracellular solution

FIGURE 3 Low oxygen concentration gradients in a mass of cells. The concentration gradient is $(C_1 - C_2)/d$. When d is large, the concentration gradient is small for a fixed value of $(C_1 - C_2)$. The red dots show oxygen concentration. The greater the difference between C_1 and C_2, the greater the concentration gradient and the rate of diffusion for a fixed value of d.

Some animals appear to contradict this rule in that they *look* as if they are more than 1 mm thick, yet have no special oxygen-transporting system of the types to be discussed shortly. However, close inspection reveals that their superficial appearance is misleading. Careful examination shows that they have structural features that keep diffusion distances less than 1 mm. Some of these animals are relatively easy to find and observe with the naked eye, for one way to keep within the 1 mm limitation is to have a very flat but very thin body. Animals such as tape-worms and their flatworm relatives are able to rely *solely* on diffusion for their oxygen supply—and a closer look at their anatomy and life-style shows how they can do this.

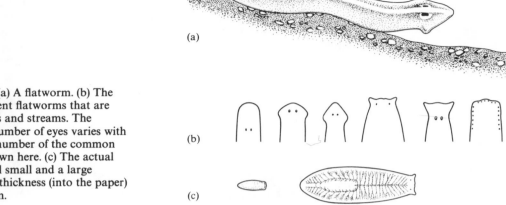

(a)

(b)

(c)

FIGURE 4 (a) A flatworm. (b) The heads of different flatworms that are found in ponds and streams. The position and number of eyes varies with the species. A number of the common species are shown here. (c) The actual size of a typical small and a large flatworm. The thickness (into the paper) is about 0.5 mm.

Flatworms (Figure 4) are found in almost every kind of freshwater from small pools to very cold mountain streams. They can also be found on the sea-shore in rock pools, and some are even terrestrial though restricted to damp areas. If you have some freshwater near you—a river, pond, or canal—go and look for flatworms. They are found on the undersides of stones (often in large numbers), on floating leaves or on submerged plants such as mosses. When still, they look like irregularly shaped lumps of jelly, but when extended they are up to 4 cm long and about 1 cm wide. Their colour can vary from white through all the shades of brown to black. Don't confuse them with the small harmless leeches which are superficially similar but have a sucker at each end. If you remove flatworms gently from the stone or leaf and place them in a glass container of fresh water, after a few minutes they should extend and start to move. They often glide with no apparent muscular movement, using very fine hairlike projections called cilia on the undersurface. They can glide upside down on the surface of the water, supported by the surface tension. You will meet cilia again in other animals, performing different functions, because cilia are widespread in animals from single-celled organisms to humans.

Most flatworms are around 0.5 mm thick. Can you suggest why flatworms don't grow up to the maximum thickness of 1 mm mentioned earlier?

As flatworms usually have one surface in contact with the 'ground', only half the body area is available for the uptake of oxygen. Therefore the maximum thickness is about half the theoretical maximum value.

Having a flat body is not the only way in which an animal can have dimensions that exceed 1 mm while keeping all cells less than 1 mm from an oxygen supply so that diffusion can take place. Look at the jellyfish in Figure 5a. At first sight it seems impossible that such a large organism could manage to obtain oxygen by diffusion alone. However, if we were to take a slice out of the animal (Figure 5b), we would see that the rather thick central mass of jelly-like tissue *has very few cells* in it—and so it does not

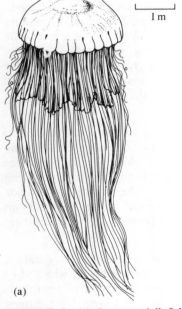

1 m

(a)

FIGURE 5 (a) *Cyanea*, a jellyfish. (b) Section of a jellyfish to show the two tissue layers, and the mass of jelly in the centre. The epidermis is a single layer of cells lining the surface. The gastrodermis is a single layer of cells lining the digestive cavity.

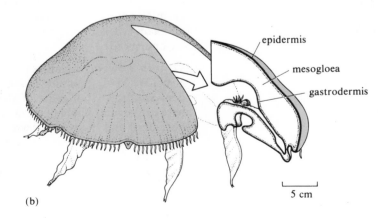

epidermis

mesogloea

gastrodermis

5 cm

(b)

7

TRACHEAL SYSTEM

SPIRACLE

ALVEOLI

matter that this mass (the mesogloea) is so far from oxygenated water. In contrast, however, the two single layers of cells surrounding the mesogloea are in continuous contact with the water. This means that the diffusion path for oxygen is short—always less than a millimetre—despite the fact that large jellyfish like *Cyanea* may grow to 3 m across! The cells within the mesogloea do use oxygen, of course, but at such a low rate that they can cope with the slow diffusion rate that results from their large distance from the surface of the animal.

2.3 OXYGEN SUPPLY IN LARGE MULTICELLULAR ORGANISMS

There are, however, a limited number of variations on the flatworm and jellyfish theme and all of them involve either thin or 'frilly' organisms in which the environmental oxygen is never very far from the layer of cells. Yet there is a very large number of species of relatively big and compact organisms that are clearly not constrained in size by the need to keep their cells within 1 mm of *the outside environment*. All of these, however, continue to ensure that all cells are within 1 mm of an *internal* fully oxygenated solution. This is achieved, depending on the type of animal, in several different ways; two are discussed below.

(i) In insects, air is taken into the animal and 'piped' by a system of tubes to every part of its body. No cell, therefore is more than 1 mm from the end of an air tube.

(ii) In others, mammals, birds and fish, for example, oxygen is taken from the environment into a fluid medium within the body, and this oxygen-containing *liquid* is circulated to within 1 mm of the cells that need oxygen.

Let us consider each of these in turn.

Insects are unusual in having a distribution system for air. Most animals, as noted above, use a circulating liquid to carry acquired oxygen. In insects, however, oxygen reaches the tissues by a system of tubes that carries the air itself through their bodies (Figure 6). This tube system is called the **tracheal system**. The tracheae open to the atmosphere through valves called **spiracles**. In small insects, air movement may be passive, but, in most, muscles contract to force air in and out of the tubes. The main tracheae have side trunks that in turn have many branches. The ends of the tracheae are very small and are very permeable to water. Most oxygen diffusion into the tissues takes place at these blind ends. Despite the anatomical complexity of the tracheal system, the underlying principle is the now familiar one of ensuring that the diffusion pathway is short.

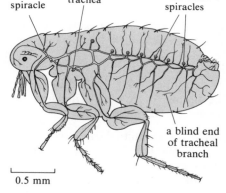

FIGURE 6 A side view of a flea, showing the internal tracheae that carry oxygen to the tissues from the spiracles. Oxygen goes into solution at the blind ends of the tracheal branches, and then diffuses to the tissues nearby.

This system of tubes provides a very efficient way to distribute oxygen to the cells in small insects. But in very active insects (the house-fly has a wing speed of about 120 beats per second), the rate at which the flight muscles consume oxygen is so great that there is an upper limit on the size of flying insects imposed by the rate at which an internal tube system can provide the huge amounts of oxygen needed. Considering the success of insects on our planet, it is perhaps just as well for us that there is an upper limit on size and speed!

We turn now to organisms that use specialized systems to oxygenate a particular kind of liquid (blood, as you will see in Section 3), which they then circulate to all parts of their bodies. Across the range of organisms there are several kinds of oxygenating organs—gills and lungs are the most specialized and the best known. Both involve exposing a *large area* of membrane to the external oxygen-rich environment, with the result that oxygen molecules diffuse across it into the underlying blood supply. This is then swept away by the circulation system (again, you will see more of this in Section 3) to more distant parts of the body.

☐ How do lungs and gills differ as regards oxygen source?

■ For organisms with gills, the oxygen-rich external environment is water. Thus diffusion occurs directly from the environment, across the gill membranes, into the blood. Organisms with lungs have air as the oxygen-rich external environment. This dissolves in the surface water on the external surfaces of the lung membrane. Thereafter, the route is as before—diffusion from the solution across the membrane into the circulating blood.

Lungs have, therefore, to capture atmospheric oxygen so that it will dissolve in water before it can enter the body by diffusion. How do they do this?

Unit 22 introduced you to the idea of respiration being the catabolic breakdown of sugars and other carbon compounds to provide energy. Physiologists, however, sometimes use the word respiration to mean the physical *process* of breathing (from the Latin *spirare*, 'to breathe'). The respiratory system in humans consists of the nose, mouth and lungs, together with the tube that links them: the trachea. During breathing, air is taken in through the nose or mouth and passes down the trachea to the lungs. Each lung consists of a series of branching tubes, each tube getting narrower at each branch. The smallest thin-walled tubes, the **alveoli**, are the sites at which oxygen diffuses into the blood. This arrangement is shown in Figure 7a. In Table 1, the sizes of the component tubes of the lung are compared, and the approximate number present in each lung is shown. The contribution of each to the total volume of air held in the lung is given (as a percentage) in the last column. You can see that 70% of the air in the lung is within the alveoli, where oxygen absorption takes place.

TABLE 1   The numbers and sizes of the tubes of the human respiratory system and the volumes of air held within them.

	Number	Diameter/mm	Volume/%
Trachea	1	18	1.7
Small bronchi	10^3	1.3	2.3
Bronchioles	10^4	0.8	3.0
Respiratory bronchioles	3×10^5	0.5	23
Alveoli	3×10^8	0.1	70

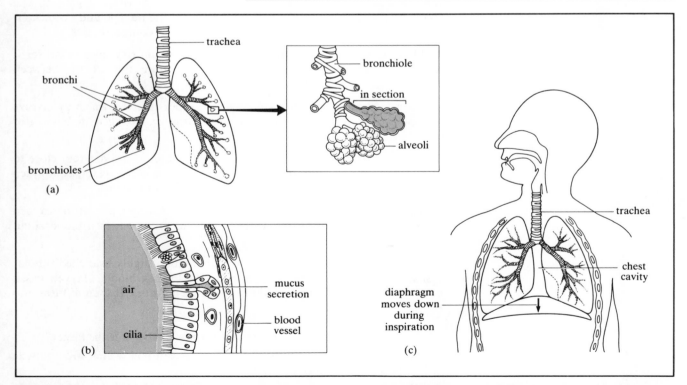

FIGURE 7   Lung structure. (a) The structure of the human lung. (b) The cells that line the bronchi, showing the cilia that remove dust and other small particles, and the cells that produce the mucus. (c) The position of the lungs in the chest cavity of a human, showing how the diaphragm moves during inspiration.

PLASMA

HAEMOGLOBIN

It is interesting to note that the air that is taken into the lungs may well contain small particles of dust that could block the alveoli. These need to be disposed of, and in the bronchioles and bronchi (singular, bronchus) there are cells with small hairs projecting from them (see Figures 7a and 7b). The hairs, called cilia, propel particles along; they are similar to the hairs that propel flatworms (Section 2.2). In the bronchioles, cilia move dust particles away from the alveoli towards the bronchi. The particles are then caught up in a sticky fluid called mucus, and it is this mucus that causes us to cough when it reaches the trachea.

The movement of air into the lung is accomplished by the muscles in the chest—in fact, the same muscles that are involved in coughing. Separating the chest from the abdomen is a muscular membrane called the diaphragm. During quiet breathing, that is when no exercise is being performed, contraction of the diaphragm muscles alters the shape of the diaphragm and it draws air into the lungs. When contraction ceases, the elasticity of the chest and lungs restores the diaphragm to its original shape and the lungs expel air (Figure 7c). During exercise, the chest muscles and the diaphragm help to draw in and expel air. The result of this movement is that there is a tidal flow of air into and out of the alveoli: a resting person inhales 5 litres of air per minute. As a consequence, fresh supplies of air are continuously being brought into contact with the $100 \, m^2$ of alveolar surface available for gaseous exchange. Blood in vessels beneath the alveoli (Figure 7b) becomes oxygenated as a result of diffusion across the walls of the alveoli and blood vessels—the diffusion distance is, as ever, small. What happens to the oxygen as it enters the blood within the lungs is a separate question that is considered in Section 3.

SUMMARY OF SECTION 2

1 Oxygen from the air dissolves in water. Small aquatic organisms can absorb this oxygen and pass it directly to all of their cells by diffusion alone.

2 The rate of diffusion of oxygen into an organism is proportional to the concentration gradient between the outside and inside of the organism. The concentration gradient is the difference between the outside and inside concentration divided by the distance between the two compartments.

3 Organisms that rely on diffusion alone to obtain oxygen and deliver it to all the cells cannot have a distance of more than 1 mm between environment and oxygen-requiring cells.

4 Larger organisms require an oxygen transport system: this may involve transport of oxygen in air (insects) or transport of oxygen in blood (for example, birds, mammals and fish).

5 Insects have a tracheal system that brings gaseous oxygen very close to the tissues. The ends of the tracheae are permeable to water, so oxygen moves through the tracheal walls to the tissues by diffusion.

6 Fish have gills with thin skin and a rich blood supply permitting oxygen molecules to diffuse from the water of their environment into blood circulating in the gills.

7 Mammals and birds have lungs that contain a highly branched tubular system that brings oxygen very close to circulating blood. Oxygen in air dissolves in a film of water on the alveolar membranes. It then diffuses into the blood.

SAQ I   Which of the following concentration gradients is the larger?

(a) The concentration gradient of oxygen between pondwater and a muscle cell 0.1 mm from the surface of a flatworm.

(b) The concentration gradient of oxygen between the same pondwater and an identical muscle cell 0.25 mm from the surface of a flatworm.

SAQ 2 Which of the following rates of oxygen diffusion is likely to be greater?

(a) The rate of diffusion from pondwater into a rapidly metabolizing cell 0.3 mm from the surface of a flatworm.

(b) The rate of diffusion from the same pondwater to a cell with very few mitochondria 0.3 mm from the surface of a flatworm.

3 CIRCULATORY SYSTEMS

Section 2 established that in large animals the supply of oxygen to each cell is not possible by passive means because the distances involved are too great. Diffusion alone would give an impossibly slow rate of oxygen transport. Thus, many animals have circulatory systems that move fluid containing oxygen to various parts of the body. The one that you will be most familiar with is the flow of blood in your own body.

> Blood has many functions, some of which you should already know, both from this Unit and from general knowledge. List as many as you can.

From what has been said already, oxygen transport is probably at the top of your list. Then, from what you know of catabolism from Unit 22, you might also have mentioned transport of glucose, fats and amino acids from the intestine to (ultimately) the cells where they are catabolized as fuel. From your knowledge of these catabolic reactions, you might have mentioned the transport of carbon dioxide, which is produced in cells and transported back to the lungs by the blood and thus eliminated. Two additional important functions that you may not be aware of will be discussed later in this Unit: the *circulation of hormones*, and the *movement of heat*. In addition, there are other functions not discussed in this Course, such as the crucial role of the blood in the body's defence mechanisms.

In this Section we shall be looking at the structure and function of the circulatory system—paying particular attention to the delivery of oxygen to metabolically active cells. Other functions of the blood—heat transport, removal of CO_2 and other products and the provision of glucose as fuel—are covered in Sections 4 and 5.

3.1 BLOOD AND OXYGEN TRANSPORT

At the end of Section 2, you read about the function of the lungs in humans. You saw how the airways in the lungs branch extensively and become narrow with the result that, at the alveoli, the diameter is only 0.1 mm, and only a very short diffusion path separates air from the blood. As a result, oxygen molecules diffuse rapidly from the solution on the surface of the alveoli, across two layers of cells (alveolar membrane and wall of blood vessel), to the watery fluid (**plasma**) of blood.

As you will see in Section 3.4, blood can carry substantially more oxygen (fifty times as much!) than would be possible if the oxygen were in simple physical solution. The reason is that red blood cells, suspended in the plasma, contain the complex protein, **haemoglobin**. This combines (reversibly) with the oxygen entering the blood vessels from the alveoli—thus decreasing plasma oxygen concentration, so allowing more oxygen to diffuse in. The oxygen-laden haemoglobin is carried away by the circulatory system to the tissues where, through the reversibility of the reaction, the oxygen is released and made available to the respiring cells.

Before we turn to the functioning of the human circulation system (in Section 3.2), it is worthwhile reminding ourselves that physiology is as diverse as the animal kingdom. For example, not all animals have haemoglobin as an oxygen-carrying molecule. Snails, squid, lobsters and their

TABLE 2 The oxygen consumption of several animals

	Oxygen consumption/ $cm^3\,g^{-1}\,min^{-1}$
sea anemone	2.3×10^{-4}
earthworm	1.0×10^{-3}
octopus	1.5×10^{-3}
frog	2.5×10^{-3}
butterfly (resting)	1.0×10^{-2}
human (walking)	3.6×10^{-2}
mouse (resting)	4.2×10^{-2}
human (running)	5.1×10^{-2}
sparrow	0.1
mouse (running)	0.330
butterfly (flying)	1.7

relatives have another pigment rather similar to haemoglobin called **haemocyanin** in their blood. The blood is colourless when deoxygenated, but greeny-blue when carrying oxygen—very different from the change from dark purple-red to bright red in haemoglobin. In Table 2 some common animals are listed in increasing order of oxygen usage. Clearly, the transport systems of some organisms must be able to meet very large demands for oxygen, whereas in others demand will be much less. As you know from Unit 21, unless some phenotypic characteristic offers a real advantage in terms of relative fitness, evolutionary change will not occur. Being able to transport oxygen at the rate achieved by a mouse is not likely to be advantageous to a sedentary snail—and it is not at all surprising that haemocyanin is able to carry much less oxygen than haemoglobin. The argument can be equally well put in converse form—the high-capacity oxygen transport systems of mammals and birds appear to be adaptations to their active modes of life.

3.2 THE HEART AND BLOOD VESSELS

The circulatory system of mammals (including humans) is a closed system with a pump—the heart. Tissues needing blood are penetrated by a network of small diameter blood vessels called **capillaries** (Figure 8a). The extremely thin walls of the capillaries allow the exchange of dissolved gases and nutrients between the blood and the cells. Blood enters the capillary network through small arteries called **arterioles**, and the latter receive blood direct from the heart via **arteries**. Blood is conveyed away from the capillaries back to the heart by **veins**. As Figure 8b shows, the walls of arteries are much thicker and more muscular than those of veins. Veins, however, are well supplied with valves that ensure blood flow is all in the same direction (Figure 8c). The vessel with the greatest resistance to flow is a capillary. The smaller the diameter of a tube, the greater its resistance to fluid flow, and the capillaries are the blood vessels with the smallest diameter. However, the proliferation of the capillary network away from an arteriole means that the overall cross-sectional area of the capillary network is greater than that of the arteriole that supplies it, and so has a lower resistance to flow than the arteriole. Thus it is the arteriole that provides the principal resistance to flow.

An average adult has a blood volume of around 5 to 6 litres (roughly 10 pints). When a person is exercising energetically, the output of blood from the heart, known as **cardiac output**, can be as much as $25\,l\,min^{-1}$. This impressive value (it is about 40% greater than the delivery rate of a petrol pump on the garage forecourt!) sounds enormous, until you realize that the muscles *need* a flow rate of that level to provide sufficient oxygen for catabolism when working hard. This rate of delivery of blood is provided by a pump weighing around 300 g which can run without pause for more than 100 years in those people who reach extreme age—a remarkable organ.

Figure 9a shows the route taken by blood through the heart. You will find it useful to study this Figure carefully while you read the following text.

The heart itself is principally composed of muscle, and you can see this very clearly in the photograph of a pig's heart in Plate 9. It has four chambers, and two streams of blood pass through the heart simultaneously. The two left chambers are completely separated from the two right ones. The **atria** act principally as reservoirs for incoming blood and pump it into the **ventricles**. The ventricles are the pumps proper. Note that 'left' and 'right' always refer to the orientation of the heart (or any organ) when it is in the body. Thus the terms are independent of the way we view it—and sometimes makes diagrams of the heart confusing at first sight. In Figure 9 the heart is viewed from the front, so the left ventricle is on the right of the diagram. The same orientation applies in the photograph in Plate 9.

When blood leaves the capillaries of the tissues in the various parts of the body, it is collected by veins and channelled back to the heart, arriving at

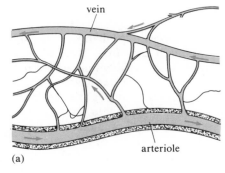
vein

arteriole

(a)

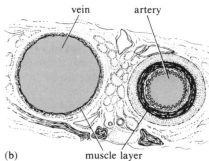
vein   artery

(b)   muscle layer

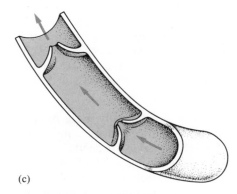
(c)

FIGURE 8 Blood vessels. (a) A network of blood capillaries connecting an arteriole to a small vein. The arrows show the direction of blood flow. (b) Cross-sections through a vein (left) and an artery (right) to show the difference in thickness of their walls. (c) A vein cut open to show the valves inside that ensure that flow is in one direction only.

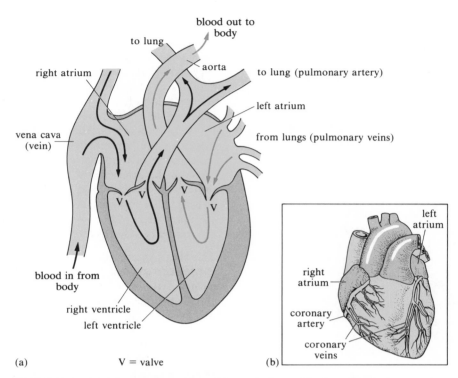

(a)   V = valve   (b)

FIGURE 9   (a) A human heart viewed from the front. The heart has been cut open to show the internal structure, including the valves that ensure that blood flow is in the right direction. The red arrows show the movement of oxygenated blood through the left side of the heart, and the black arrows the movement of deoxygenated blood. (b) An intact human heart showing the coronary blood vessels. These supply blood to the heart muscle, which needs a constant supply of oxygen and metabolites as it is always working.

the right atrium via the **vena cava**. A modestly powerful contraction of the right atrium then forces blood into the right ventricle which, consequently, expands. (Back-flow is prevented by the valves you saw in Figure 8c.) This is followed by a powerful contraction in the thick muscular walls of the right ventricle, and the pressurized blood is forced along the pulmonary arteries to the lungs and through the arterioles forming part of the **pulmonary circulation** to the capillaries of the alveoli. Note that back-flow of the blood into the right atrium as a result of the contraction of the ventricle is prevented (except in those with certain heart defects) by a further set of valves between the two right-hand chambers.

Look at Figure 10 and you will see that the part of the **double circulation** so far discussed is shown by black arrows—denoting the route of deoxygenated blood. The pulmonary circulation takes blood through the lungs where gas exchange takes place: carbon dioxide, carried there by blood from the tissues, passes *into* the alveoli; the oxygen passes *out* of the alveoli into the blood ready for transport (via the heart) to the tissues.

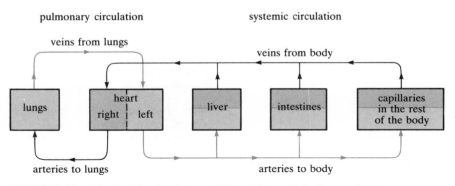

FIGURE 10   The double circulation of blood through the human heart. Oxygen-rich blood is shown as red arrows, deoxygenated blood as black arrows.

AORTA

SYSTEMIC CIRCULATION

TELEOLOGICAL STATEMENT

At this point blood pressure is low. If you think back to the discussion of diffusion and gas exchange in Section 2.3, you will appreciate that the very large gas-exchanging area in the lungs ($100 \, m^2$ was cited earlier) requires a very extensive capillary supply. Once blood has passed through such a network of narrow vessels, its pressure is necessarily low. If the freshly oxygenated blood leaving the lungs in the pulmonary veins is to be successfully delivered to body tissues, it must be re-pressurized—hence the return part of the pulmonary circulation. Blood re-enters the heart at the left atrium, passes to the left ventricle (again via valves) and, by dint of the powerful contraction of the muscles of the left ventricle, is forced out, via the **aorta**, through the arteries and arterioles of the **systemic circulation** to the tissues that await fresh supplies of oxygen and glucose. The heart, being mostly muscle, also requires oxygen and glucose, and it receives blood via the coronary artery. The blood returns to the chambers of the heart through the coronary vein (Figure 9b).

The heart pumps 50–75 times a minute in a resting human adult. The blood is pressurized each time the heart pumps, so the flow from the heart is not steady, but fluctuates with the heart beat. Despite this uneven heart output, the tissues need a steady supply of blood to work efficiently—and this is achieved in part through the considerable elasticity of the walls of the arteries. The flexible walls of the arteries expand as the heart pressurizes the blood, and then 'rebound' when the pressure reduces, thus smoothing out flow. In doing this, they *store* strain energy (Unit 9, Section 2.3) during the heart beat, and then convert the stored energy to kinetic energy (Unit 9, Section 6), which is transferred to the passing blood between beats. To reduce unnecessary strain on the heart, one might have expected large arteries with consequently low resistance would have arisen through evolution. However, large arteries would entail transport of a large mass of blood—putting strain upon the pump in yet another way. In fact the outcome is a compromise—reflecting, probably, the situation that confers the greatest fitness.

Both these points, elasticity and internal diameter, are examples of the strong relationship between structure and function that one sees at all levels of biology. In physiology, this relationship is often so strongly apparent that so-called **teleological statements** are easily made. 'Alveoli have a large surface area *so that* they can exchange gases readily' is an example that you will appreciate from Section 2.3. A teleological statement is one that implies design for a *purpose*, and you should avoid writing in this way as it is, however convenient, biologically incorrect.

☐ What should you write instead of 'arteries are elastic in order to smooth out the pulses of pressure from the heart'?

◼ You need something of this type: 'it is likely that smooth blood flow as a consequence of flexible artery walls has proved evolutionarily advantageous'. Or, more briefly: 'blood flow is smooth because artery walls are flexible'.

In fact, many biologists do write teleological statements as a matter of convenient shorthand: you may find some have slipped through in these Units! You will certainly hear plenty in various open network television programmes on natural history—spoken, often, by quite eminent biologists! One may assume, however, that they *are* aware that it is natural selection and not design for a purpose that accounts for the marvel of the buoyancy swim-bladder of fish, the long insect-catching tongue of a chameleon, or the functional appropriateness of mammalian double circulation.

Now that the essential 'plumbing' arrangements of the human circulatory system have been examined, we can return to the continuing theme of oxygen supply to tissues. As noted earlier, a major aim of the Unit is to consider the mechanisms of physiological regulation and control—and, with that in mind, we will look at human response to mild exercise.

3.3 THE PHYSIOLOGICAL DEMANDS OF EXERCISE (EXPERIMENT)

In the following experiment you will investigate what happens to the heart and circulatory system during exercise. To do this you either need to make observations on yourself, or persuade some *fit and healthy* friend or relative to be your subject.

If, for any reason, it would be unwise for you to exercise in the way described below, you should look for someone to act as your subject.

EXPERIMENT

INVESTIGATING THE EFFECT OF EXERCISE ON THE HUMAN HEART RATE

TIME
This experiment takes about 45 minutes

NON-KIT ITEMS

A stop-watch or clock that displays seconds.

Your body (or that of a fit subject)

A step to provide exercise for you or your assistant.

KIT ITEMS

None required for this experiment

You will be measuring heart rate by taking your pulse or that of your subject, before, during and after a period of exercise. Before starting the experiment you will need to practise taking your own pulse. You should read through the complete experiment before you start, since you will need to decide on the amount of exercise to take and also to prepare a Table in your Notebook in which to enter the results.

PRACTICE SESSION

Find the pulsating blood vessel passing over the bone of your wrist in the position shown under the middle fingers in Figure 11. (Use your fingers, not your thumb.) You may well need to press quite hard, and you will probably find it a little difficult at first. Once you are quite sure that you can feel the pulse reliably, sit in a position where you can conveniently carry out the timing. You are going to measure your own resting pulse rate.

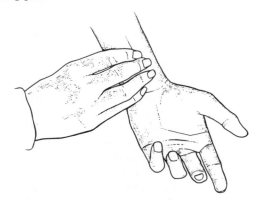

FIGURE 11   How to take your pulse.

Start the stop-watch (or look at the clock). Feel a pulse and at a convenient position of the second-hand begin to count. Stop the watch (or read the clock) when you have counted thirty-one beats of the pulse. Record the time taken for 30 beats. Heart rate is normally recorded as 'beats per minute', so you should express the time for 30 beats as the equivalent number of beats per minute. If you are unsure how to do this, try ITQ 1.

ITQ 1   Suppose that the time taken for 30 beats is 40 seconds. What is the equivalent heart rate in beats minute^{-1}?

ITQ 2   Why do you stop the watch on the thirty-first pulse?

EXPERIMENT CONTINUED

EXPERIMENTAL PROCEDURE

First you need to draw up a Table in your Notebook to record your results.

Sit quietly for five minutes. Now take three measurements of pulse rate while still at rest and record each measurement in your Table.

Convert your results to beats per minute and calculate the average resting heart rate. Enter this result in your Table.

Now take the exercise. Climb onto and off a step the size of a normal staircase step around 100 times. You might have to adjust the speed of exercise or the number of steps to suit your own fitness. The aim of the experiment is not to produce exhaustion, but a fit person might not find 100 steps sufficient exercise to make a substantial change in their heart rate. *Only do what you know is safe and suitable for you or your subject.*

Immediately exercise is complete, measure and record the pulse rate. Take a further measurement of pulse rate starting 2 minutes after the end of the exercise period. Take a third measurement at 5 minutes, and a fourth at 10 minutes. You will only be able to measure each of these pulse rates once. Enter these results in your Table.

You have now completed the experiment, but remember to check that you have all the details you need to answer any associated assignment questions.

You should have found that exercise increases heart rate, and that the heart rate does not slow down as soon as the exercise stops. Assuming relative fitness, then the resting pulse rate will probably fall in the range of around 50–75 beats per minute, and your first reading after exercise stops is likely to be around 120–180 beats per minute. This is the usual range for most people: others—who are nonetheless entirely healthy—may have values of less than 120 or more than 180 beats per minute.

Now this increased rate means that the amount of blood being pumped by the heart (the cardiac output, you remember) has increased during exercise. In fact the increase would have been from around 5.5 litres min^{-1} to 25 litres min^{-1} during heavy exercise. This increase is due not only to the increase in *rate*, but also to an increase in **stroke volume**—that is, the volume of blood pumped out by the heart during a contraction: around 80 cm^3 at rest, rising to 140 cm^3 during exercise. There is a simple relationship between cardiac output, stroke volume and heart rate:

$$\text{cardiac output} = \text{stroke volume} \times \text{heart rate} \qquad (2)$$

As an example, take the figure of 70 beats min^{-1} at rest, and the stroke volume of 80 cm^3:

$$\text{cardiac output} = 80\,cm^3 \times 70\,\text{beats}\,min^{-1} = 5\,600\,cm^3\,min^{-1}$$

$$= 5.6\,\text{litres}\,min^{-1}\ (\text{because 1 litre} = 1\,000\,cm^3)$$

ITQ 3 During heavy exercise, the heart rate of an athlete was measured as 170 beats min^{-1}. If the athlete's cardiac output was 25 litres min^{-1}, what was the stroke volume of the heart (in cm^3)?

Having measured heart rate yourself, you may be wondering how figures for cardiac output can be measured in a human without major surgery. They can, in fact, be measured by a fairly simple procedure that depends on injecting a dye into a vein, followed by the collection of a number of blood samples. The method, used regularly to investigate certain heart defects, is included here to illustrate how internal physiological data can be found in living subjects.

STROKE VOLUME

COLORIMETER

By determining how fast the injected dye is circulated and then by how much it is diluted, cardiac output can be calculated. Look at Figure 12a to see what is going on. 5 milligrams of blue dye is injected into a vein at point I. From this point it travels to the heart, on through the lungs, back to the heart and out into the arteries. The amount of dye in the blood is sampled by drawing off a series of samples every 30 seconds through a cannula (a sort of tap pushed into an artery) at point S. Dye concentration is measured in a machine termed a **colorimeter**: a beam of light passes through the sample and the amount of light transmitted is related to the concentration of the dye. If the concentration of the dye in each sample is plotted against time for a person who exercises continuously throughout the test, the red curve in Figure 12b is obtained. A resting subject produces a curve of the type shown by the black line.

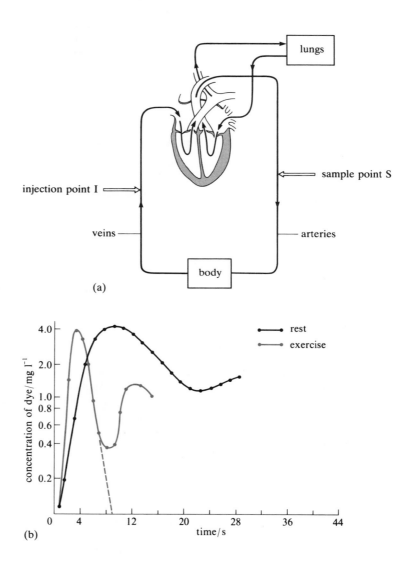

FIGURE 12 Measurement of cardiac output in a human. (a) Injection of dye into bloodstream at point I and sampling at point S: arrows show the route taken by the dye. (b) Dye concentration in blood samples from a person at rest (black line) and exercising (red line).

ITQ 4 Imagine a local 'cloud of blue dye' in the blood near point I and picture what happens as that blood moves through the blood vessels towards point S.

(a) Why does the dye level rise, fall and then rise again?

(b) Why does the peak in the exercise curve occur earlier than in the rest curve?

With the answer to this ITQ in mind, how can we calculate (from the results in Figure 12b) how fast the dye is circulated? You can determine this directly for the exercise curve, by measuring the time taken for the cloud of dye to travel from S, right round the system and back to S again. As you see, it is 9 seconds—the distance between the two peaks. In fact, it is usually more convenient to measure the time from 'no dye at all' (the origin of the graph) to 'no dye at all, again'. You have to find the latter by extending the downwards part of the first peak to the baseline.

☐ The exercise curve has been extended for you (shown as a dashed line in Figure 12b). At what time does it cross the baseline? What conclusions do you draw?

■ It crosses after 9 seconds. This is the same as the time between the two peaks.

So the cloud of dye in the blood circulates in 9 seconds—but how much blood is there in that cloud of dye? As noted earlier, we can find this by seeing how much blood must have been involved in diluting the injected dye (5 mg of it, remember) to the concentration of it in the cloud. The latter value is not straightforwardly obtained: it is very dilute at the edges of the cloud and concentrated at the centre (the curve's peak). By combining data from the 30 samples, an average dye concentration can be calculated.

☐ From the full set of data for the 30 samples (not given here), the calculated average dye concentration is $1.5\,mg\,l^{-1}$. 5 mg was injected. What must have been the blood volume in the dye cloud?

■ This is calculated as follows: 5 mg (mass of dye injected) divided by V (volume of blood in the cloud of dye) equals $1.5\,mg\,l^{-1}$ (average concentration of dye in the cloud of dye). Hence, $V \approx 3.33$ litres.

The end part of the calculations associated with the procedure is now very easy. 3.33 litres of blood circulated in 9 seconds. Therefore $(3.33/9) \times 60$ litres of blood circulated in one minute. The calculated result, 22.2 litres, is the cardiac output.

ITQ 5 What is the cardiac output for the resting curve in Figure 12b? (This time you will have to extend the line to determine circulation time, as a second peak is not present.) You are given that the average dye concentration is $1.6\,mg\,l^{-1}$, and you should remember that 5 mg of dye were injected.

The difference between cardiac output in the resting and exercising subjects is, as you see, striking—the latter is nearly five times as great. This is a direct consequence (as you will see when we examine control mechanisms) of increased oxygen demand. Let us return, therefore, to the matter of oxygen transport.

3.4 BLOOD CELLS AND HAEMOGLOBIN

Section 3.1 introduced the idea that haemoglobin is able to transport much larger quantities of oxygen than would be possible in merely physical solution. But how does it do this, and where is the haemoglobin in blood?

In the discussion of heart function, blood was treated as if it were just a liquid. It is, however, more complex than that. Blood contains cells and cell fragments of several types (Plate 10). **Platelets** are part of the clotting mechanism that seals wounds, and not only the wounds that we are aware of. They plug small holes that continuously appear in the walls of blood capillaries, for example. **White cells** have several functions concerned with protection against infection. **Red cells** are the most numerous type of blood cell, and their principal function is to transport oxygen and carbon dioxide. It is these that contain the haemoglobin molecules. Unlike white cells, both platelets and the red cells of mammals have no nuclei. The liquid component of blood is called the plasma. It is an aqueous solution of inorganic salts, containing proteins that, among other functions, help to maintain the water balance between cells and blood.

As you see from Plate 10, the human red cell has the shape of a biconcave disc. The cell membrane is very elastic, and the cells can undergo considerable deformation without damage. This is a necessary property for cells that are going to be forced through very narrow diameter tubes. The shape of the cell aids its role as a transport agent for gases. The average diameter is 7 μm, and the surface area is 140 μm². If the contents of the cell were contained in a sphere, the surface area would be smaller—thus, the biconcave shape provides a much greater area over which gas diffusion can take place. Both of these features—elasticity and shape—are further examples of the relationship of structure to function at the physiological level.

Haemoglobin within red blood cells is able to combine with and thus transport both oxygen and carbon dioxide. The latter will be discussed again in Section 4, when the removal of metabolic products is discussed. For now let us focus on oxygen transport. Look at Figure 13. This is a simplified drawing of the haemoglobin structure that you met in Unit 22 (Plate 2). The rather large molecule (its relative molecular mass is about 66 000) consists, you may remember, of four polypeptide chains. This constitutes the **globin** part of the molecule. Attached to each of these is a **haem** group. The whole molecule is usually written as Hb. (Note that Hb is *not* an element but is a generally accepted abbreviation for haemoglobin.) These haem groups are shown in red in the Figure. Each haem group, which consists of a nitrogen-containing ring structure in the centre of which is an atom of iron(II), is able to bind one oxygen molecule. Overall, therefore, one haemoglobin molecule is able to bind, in a fully *reversible* way, four oxygen molecules thus:

$$Hb + 4O_2 \rightleftharpoons HbO_8 \tag{3}$$

haemoglobin oxyhaemoglobin

FIGURE 13 The structure of haemoglobin A, showing the four polypeptide chains constituting globin, and the four associated haem groups. This is a simplification of the model shown in Plate 2 of Unit 22.

Note that the iron remains as iron(II) when this oxygen binding reaction occurs.* Haemoglobin containing oxidized iron (iron(III)) is abnormal and is biologically inactive; in fact, red cells contain enzymes whose specific function it is to ensure that the haemoglobin iron remains as iron(II). It is this reaction that gives blood the tremendously large oxygen-carrying power mentioned in Section 3.1: plasma alone can carry only 5 cm³ per litre compared with 200 cm³ per litre of whole blood. Table 3 lists the latter along with other characteristics of blood.

TABLE 3 Some characteristics of human blood. Values are averages for an adult male: there is variation between individuals

number of red cells	$5.5 \times 10^{12} \, l^{-1}$
haemoglobin content	$155 \, g \, l^{-1}$
oxygen carrying capacity	$200 \, cm^3 \, l^{-1}$
typical oxygen content of arterial blood	$195 \, cm^3 \, l^{-1}$
typical oxygen content of venous blood	$150 \, cm^3 \, l^{-1}$
plasma pH of arterial blood	7.40
plasma pH of venous blood	7.37

When arterial blood reaches the tissues, it gives up oxygen (Equation 3). It does this *because* oxygen concentration in the extracellular fluid is low as a direct consequence of mitochondrial activity in adjacent cells. Diffusion of oxygen along a concentration gradient—exactly the story you are familiar with from Section 2—now occurs.

Table 3 contains a further important and intriguing item of data. Look at the values for oxygen in arterial blood and oxygen in venous blood.

☐ Compare these values. What can you conclude?

■ Only part of the oxygen carried in the arteries of the systemic circulation is given up when it reaches the tissues.

---

* This contrasts with the situation with the cytochromes described in Unit 22. There, the reduced forms contained iron(II) and the oxidized forms iron(III).

VISCOSITY

CARBONIC ANHYDRASE

Although venous blood contains *less* oxygen than arterial blood ($150 \, cm^3 \, l^{-1}$ compared with $195 \, cm^3 \, l^{-1}$), it still contains a good deal. This means that in most tissues of the body arterial blood gives up only about a quarter of its total oxygen content in the tissue, leaving a large reserve that can be called upon in times of strenuous exercise.

☐ In Section 3.3 you came across two other ways in which the circulatory system can respond to the demands of exercise. What were they?

■ Heart rate and stroke volume can increase. The ability to yield up extra oxygen, referred to above, is a third response.

As we draw towards the close of this Section, it is useful to look at yet another example of the adaptation of structure to function. You may possibly have wondered why haemoglobin is inside the red cells rather than free in plasma solution. At first sight, simple solution in the plasma might seem advantageous in terms of 'loading and unloading' oxygen since there is one membrane less for the oxygen molecules to traverse. However, there are a number of physical and chemical factors that, one may speculate, have perhaps favoured the evolution of 'membrane-bound packets'—red cells, that is. On somewhat safer ground than evolutionary speculation, it is certainly possible to list the *consequences* of postulating the absence of red cells.

(a) The **viscosity** of the blood would be very much higher if the haemoglobin were free in the plasma. Viscosity is a measure of the resistance to flow of a liquid. Upset a cup of tea, and the tea appears to flow all over the place almost instantly. However, knock over a cup of treacle and you should be able to pick it up again long before all the treacle has flowed out. At room temperature, treacle has a much higher viscosity than tea. Increased viscosity in the plasma would offer a greater resistance to flow and so require a much stronger pump.

(b) A number of red cell enzymes catalyse reactions involving haemoglobin: an example mentioned earlier is that involved in keeping iron in its iron(II) form. It is difficult to see how these could interact effectively with haemoglobin molecules if the latter were not confined within the cell membrane.

(c) A number of molecules synthesized within the red cell alter the affinity of haemoglobin for oxygen, and are significantly involved with regulating the release of oxygen. Though such detail cannot be discussed here, these systems, also, could not readily function in a cell-less system.

This concludes our review of circulation in relation to oxygen transport. Oxygen is, of course, just one component of the oxidative equation we have chosen to guide our discussion of physiology. Logic, in the sense of dealing with the *reactants* of Equation 1 (Section 2) might seem to suggest that glucose provision should be our next concern. In fact, as the generation of CO_2 is so closely related to the consumption of oxygen, it is to that side of the equation we turn in Section 4.

SUMMARY OF SECTION 3

1 The circulatory system in mammals has functions including the supply of oxygen and oxidizable substances to cells, and the removal of metabolic products and of heat.

2 The heart provides a double circulation. The pulmonary circulation and systemic circulation are separately pumped by the heart.

3 The cardiac output alters with demand. Both heart rate and stroke volume can vary.

4 Cardiac output can be measured by injecting dye and following the progressive dilution of the dye during each circuit of the blood system.

5 Blood consists of plasma, platelets, white cells and red cells. The red cells contain haemoglobin, which has the ability to combine *reversibly* with

oxygen (and carbon dioxide) at the lungs and again at the capillaries in the tissues.

6   The presence of red cells alters the viscosity of the blood. Haemoglobin is confined within the cells, and this reduces viscosity.

7   The physiology of the circulatory system provides many examples of the close relationship of structure to function.

8   Such structure–function relationships are accounted for in terms of the theory of evolution by natural selection. Teleological statements ascribing purpose are to be avoided.

SAQ 3 Which two of the following statements about the mammalian heart and circulatory system are true?
(a) All arteries carry oxygen-rich blood.
(b) Most veins carry oxygen-depleted blood.
(c) All the blood passes through the lungs, but not all passes through the heart.
(d) In the heart the blood passes from the atria into the ventricles, but the chambers on each side are separated so there are two independent flow routes taken by the blood.

SAQ 4 In the experiment, you should have found that the heart rate did not immediately return to the resting level after the exercise stopped. Suggest a possible biochemical reason for this.

SAQ 5 Why is it advantageous that blood should have low viscosity?

4 REMOVING THE PRODUCTS OF METABOLISM

There remains from Equation 1 (Section 2) the question of what happens to carbon dioxide and water. Also, from Unit 22, Section 7, which dealt with other fuels than glucose, you should recall that there will be waste nitrogen compounds to dispose of. Finally, associated with ATP production and usage there will be metabolic heat to be dissipated. This Section considers the ways in which organisms remove the products of metabolism.

4.1 DISPOSAL OF CARBON DIOXIDE

Virtually all the carbon dioxide produced as the result of metabolism diffuses directly into the bloodstream. Therefore, the blood transports it to the lungs, into which it is released by diffusion and from which it is discharged in exhaled breath.

In Unit 22 you were shown the precise relationship between the amount of oxygen used during catabolism, and the amount of carbon dioxide formed. Carbon dioxide reacts with water, as shown in Equation 4:

$$CO_2 + H_2O \rightleftharpoons \underset{\text{bicarbonate ion}}{H^+ + HCO_3^-} \tag{4}$$

Most of the CO_2 produced in the tissues during catabolism is transported to the lungs in the form of bicarbonate ions. In the red cells the enzyme **carbonic anhydrase** catalyses the formation of H^+ and HCO_3^- from H_2O and CO_2. So the reaction goes much faster in the red cells than in the plasma, where there is no carbonic anhydrase. The two ions produced are quickly removed from solution in the cells since the H^+ is taken up by the haemoglobin, and the HCO_3^- diffuses back into the blood plasma where its concentration is lower.

□ How do you think it is possible for haemoglobin to take up H^+ ions?

■ As with many proteins, there are many *R groups* along the polypeptide chain that, being ionized, can take up hydrogen ions.

This continuing process of bicarbonate formation followed by its diffusion into plasma maintains a CO_2 concentration gradient between the respiring tissues (high CO_2 concentration) and the red cells (low CO_2 concentration due to bicarbonate formation). Study Figure 14, which summarizes this sequence of reactions. At the lungs, the hydrogen ions taken up by the haemoglobin during the passage of the blood through the tissues are released again. These react with the bicarbonate ions of the plasma to give water and CO_2.

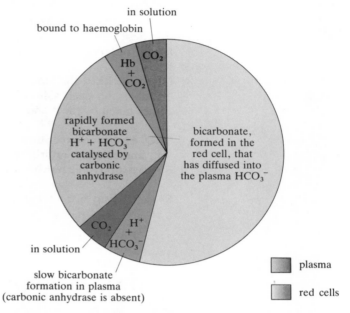

FIGURE 14   The removal of carbon dioxide from tissues by the formation of HCO_3^- in the red cells, which then passes into the plasma. The pie diagram shows the percentage of carbon dioxide in each of the different categories: for example, about 70% of carbon dioxide is in the plasma.

□ How do you think the CO_2 leaves the capillaries of the alveoli?

■ By diffusion along a concentration gradient: once free as a gas in the alveolar spaces, it is breathed out during exhalation.

This sequence of reactions is important because, by forming HCO_3^-, carbon dioxide can be carried in the blood. The acidification of the blood resulting from this dissociation, which alters its pH (Table 3, Section 3.4), forms the basis of the mechanism used by the body to detect increased tissue respiration and hence the need for an increase in breathing rate. We shall be considering the control of breathing rate further in Section 6.

4.2 ELIMINATION OF WATER AND NITROGEN COMPOUNDS

As CO_2 is blown out of the lungs to get rid of it, so some water is also lost by evaporation from the alveolar surface. However, this route only accounts for about 2% of the total water loss in a person at rest at 20 °C; most is lost by other ways.

ITQ 6   From general knowledge, list routes by which the human body loses water.

$$O=C \begin{cases} NH_2 \\ NH_2 \end{cases}$$

urea

One of the routes by which water is lost is via the bladder. The main nitrogen-containing compound of human* urine is **urea**, an organic compound whose molecular structure is shown in the margin. Water is also lost in other ways, for example by sweating (see Section 6) and, indeed, by breathing, in which water evaporates from the surface of the alveoli.

Where does the nitrogen in urine come from?

One source is the catabolism of amino acids: the NH_2 group is split off each amino acid molecule and then converted (by another metabolic pathway) to urea. You have met deamination (removing amino groups from amino acids) in Unit 22, Section 7. The non-nitrogen parts that are left, you may remember, are dealt with by the central pathways—giving CO_2, H_2O, ATP and heat in the usual way.

Waste nitrogen compounds must be removed, as in high concentrations they are damaging. However, as urea has to be disposed of in solution, an inevitable consequence is that water is lost from the body. The kidneys remove urea from the bloodstream, where it has a concentration of about $300\,mg\,l^{-1}$, and forms a more concentrated fluid (urine) for disposal. The urea concentration in urine can be as high as $20\,g\,l^{-1}$.

We have now looked at the supply of oxygen and, though only briefly, the disposal of wastes: CO_2, water, and nitrogen compounds. These are all the major products of catabolism except one—heat.

4.3 HEAT TRANSFER

All organisms produce heat as a consequence of their metabolic activity. You know from Unit 22, Section 6.1, that—except when doing external work (the transfer of gravitational or kinetic energy in lifting or throwing, for example)—*all* the energy released in catabolism ultimately appears as heat. Thus, if you eat food that yields $10\,000\,kJ$ on oxidation, all of it (apart from any expended on external objects) will ultimately appear as metabolic heat. It is this, in terms of Equation 1, that seems at first sight to be an unwanted product. In fact, however, the term 'waste' is not wholly appropriate when applied to heat. It is plain from general knowledge of the world around us, that heat is important to all organisms—in the sense that retained heat increases body temperature and heat disposal reduces body temperature.

☐ Why, in all groups of organisms, is it important that internal temperature should neither be too low nor too high?

■ The rate of any chemical reaction increases with temperature. At temperatures lower than normal (for a particular organism), biochemical reactions, hence bodily activities, would occur at a lower than normal rate. If body temperature is too high, proteins become denatured (Unit 22, Section 4.3), leading ultimately to death.

In some animals (those described as 'cold-blooded' in everyday language), heat production through their own, rather slow, metabolic processes is often inadequate for their temperature needs. Such organisms—lizards, for example—frequently *take in* heat by moving into a warm part of the environment, moving out of it when they are warm enough: a simple but often very effective kind of control. It is also plain that for organisms of this type, 'getting rid of metabolic heat' is no problem at all: metabolic rate is so low, in comparative terms.

* In other taxonomic groups the principle nitrogen compound excreted may be other than urea. For example, it is ammonia (NH_3) in fish and uric acid (a more complex organic nitrogen molecule) in birds and reptiles. Uric acid is rather insoluble and is the white powdery constituent of bird lime.

HYPOGLYCAEMIA

HEPATIC PORTAL VEIN

Birds and mammals are the two groups of organisms that maintain a constant inner temperature. As we shall see later, the regulatory systems that have evolved are quite complex—being able to maintain temperature constancy in the core of the body *either* when heat loss is high and heat production is low (when asleep in cold weather, for example) *or* when heat loss is low and heat production is high (when running in hot sun, for example). Sometimes, therefore, heat must be produced and conserved; on other occasions, it must be disposed of to the environment.

Section 6 considers, in some detail, how the balance between 'heat in' and 'heat out' is achieved. The point of importance at present is that blood has a crucial role in the transfer of heat from the tissues in which it is catabolically generated via the detectors of temperature that form part of the control system, to the skin from which heat is lost to the environment.

SUMMARY OF SECTION 4

1 Carbon dioxide is produced in the cells as a result of metabolism, and is transported to the lungs in the bloodstream.

2 Very little CO_2 can be carried in solution in the blood plasma, but the enzyme carbonic anhydrase in the red cells catalyses the formation of bicarbonate, which increases the carrying capacity of the blood.

3 Bicarbonate is reconverted to CO_2 in the lung capillaries and passes to the alveoli by diffusion.

4 In humans (and in some other organisms) waste nitrogen is removed, in solution, in the form of urea by the kidneys. This results in a water loss since the concentration of urea in the urine is limited.

5 Water is lost through urine production, sweating and evaporation of alveolar water.

6 Blood has an important role in transporting metabolic heat and is an important part of systems that some animals employ in maintaining a constant body temperature.

5 SUPPLY OF GLUCOSE

As you saw in Unit 22, Section 6, glucose is a major source of energy in the cell. It has special significance because certain areas such as the brain are particularly sensitive to a reduced supply of glucose. The brain cells need glucose as a substrate for metabolism, yet do not themselves store glycogen.

What is the significance of the lack of glycogen stores in the brain cells?

Glucose is converted to glycogen in most tissues, notably liver and muscle. Glycogen, you will remember, is a long chain polymer of glucose, and it is relatively insoluble in blood. The glycogen acts as a glucose store—the muscles of an adult human male may contain up to 150 g of glycogen, and the liver 60 g. As no glycogen is stored by the brain cells, they are *totally dependent on the direct supply of glucose from the blood*. In this Section you will see how the level of glucose circulating in the blood is regulated, and you will discover some of the consequences of impaired regulation in humans.

5.1 REGULATION OF BLOOD GLUCOSE LEVELS

The level of glucose in the blood is relatively easy to measure, as you will see in the TV programme associated with this Unit. The normal level of blood glucose in humans before breakfast is $4.5–5.5\,\text{mmol}\,\text{l}^{-1}$ (810–990 mg l^{-1}). After a meal that contains carbohydrates (for example, corn-flakes with milk and sugar) the level will rise temporarily to around $7\,\text{mmol}\,\text{l}^{-1}$. Going without food for 24 hours will cause the level to fall to a value close to $3.5\,\text{mmol}\,\text{l}^{-1}$, but the value will not fall further even if fasting is prolonged. This is principally to protect the brain cells, because **hypogly-caemia** (low glucose level) is rapidly damaging.

As Figure 15 shows, the level of glucose measured in the blood is largely the balance of inflow from the intestine against outflow into the cells. Glucose, fructose and other sugars are the final products of the digestion of carbo-hydrates in the intestine. These diffuse out of the intestine into the capil-laries that run through the intestinal wall and are carried into the **hepatic portal vein**. This vein takes blood to the liver direct from the intestine. In the liver, fructose and other sugars are converted to glucose which is either stored as glycogen or liberated into the bloodstream.

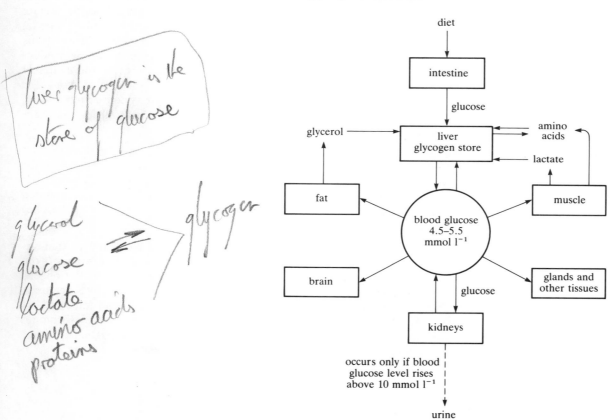

FIGURE 15 The regulation of blood glucose by the liver. There is almost total reabsorption of glucose from the urine within the kidney, to minimize loss. Only if the blood glucose level gets very high is a significant amount of glucose lost in the urine.

It is the liver that plays the key role in adjusting the level of blood glucose and thus regulating supply to match demand. This role is summarized in Figure 15, and is also considered in the TV programme, when the results from blood glucose measurements are discussed.

5.2 RESPONSES TO LOW BLOOD GLUCOSE LEVELS

There are several ways in which the body responds to low levels of blood glucose. The obvious first response is the feeling of hunger that is generated. Eating is a fast way to raise blood glucose levels. The other major responses are **glycogenolysis** and **gluconeogenesis**.

Glycogenolysis is the breakdown of glycogen to glucose, and it occurs in the liver within minutes of the blood glucose level falling to a dangerous level. The adult human liver, you remember, normally contains about 60 g of glycogen, and, if all this were metabolized, around 1 000 kJ of energy would be provided. Though this is not a lot by comparison with the total daily requirement of energy, it does give a short-term protection to the brain and other tissues without glycogen stores. For comparison, a typical daily requirement for an adult human male of 40–50 years of age weighing 65 kg is 12 600 kJ day^{-1}.

Glycogenolysis provides a short-term protective response, by providing glucose from glycogen. In contrast, gluconeogenesis provides a less rapid but longer-term solution. The term means the new ('neo') synthesis ('genesis') of glucose ('gluco'). Thus it involves the synthesis of glucose from other molecules. Glucose can be synthesized in the body from (a) lactate that is derived from muscles, (b) glycerol from the breakdown of fats, (c) certain amino acids, after the amino group has been removed. Most of this synthesis takes place in the liver, and about 180 g of glucose can be produced in 24 hours. This sounds a good deal, but if there were no food available and if therefore this 180 g were the *only* source of glucose, it would be barely sufficient. Of this 180 g, the brain and nervous system require 140 g, and 30 g is needed by the red cells—not leaving much at all for the other tissues, particularly the big consumers like muscle.

Thus, muscles—and remember that the heart is almost entirely muscle—need an alternative source of energy when glucose is in short supply. In particular, they utilize fatty acids that yield much ATP when catabolized by the β-oxidation pathway of the muscle mitochondria. In contrast, as noted earlier, the cells in the brain and nervous system are unable to metabolize *any* energy source apart from glucose.

Both gluconeogenesis and glycogenolysis are initiated by chemicals that circulate in the blood. These chemical messengers are called **hormones** (from the Greek *hormaein*, 'to excite'). More is said about these in Section 5.4. Many processes within animals and plants are controlled by hormones. These are produced in small quantities, often in certain special cells, and are generally transported to the place where they have their effect. Hormones are often very specific in their action, affecting only a particular tissue within an animal. This tissue is called the **target tissue** for that hormone.

5.3 EFFECT OF HIGH BLOOD GLUCOSE LEVELS

Hyperglycaemia, raised blood glucose level, is not of itself harmful—but the consequences may be if the effect is prolonged. In people with diabetes, the resting blood glucose level may be as high as 11 mmol l^{-1}, rising to 22–28 mmol l^{-1} after a meal, compared with the normal figures of 4.5–5.5 mmol l^{-1} at rest and 7 mmol l^{-1} after a meal. A consequence of hyperglycaemia (above 10 mmol l^{-1}) is that the kidney no longer reabsorbs all glucose and thus glucose appears in the urine. As in the case of urea, glucose has to be disposed of in solution. The glucose loss increases the amount of water lost, and so dehydration of the body may result. Dehydration produces thirst, and an increase in water intake. Important ions such as sodium and chloride are washed out with the glucose in the urine. Excessive loss of ions and water can lead to coma and death.

Thus hyperglycaemia has adverse effects and, as you saw earlier, hypoglycaemia is equally to be avoided. How, then, is the level to be maintained within narrow limits?

5.4 HORMONES AND THE REGULATION OF BLOOD GLUCOSE LEVELS

A detailed answer to this question must be postponed until Section 6, where regulatory systems are considered in some detail. However, it is useful to remind ourselves here that glucose levels are markedly affected—in one direction or the other—by several different kinds of hormone that are secreted into the blood. These—acting on glycolysis, gluconeogenesis, the uptake of glucose by cells, and on still other processes—have a powerful effect on blood glucose level. The three principal hormones involved in the regulation of blood glucose levels in humans are as follows.

1 **Glucagon** causes glycogenolysis in the liver, and increases the rate of gluconeogenesis. Because it raises blood glucose level, it is said to have a *hyperglycaemic effect*.

2 **Adrenalin** promotes glycogenolysis in liver and muscle and, therefore, is also hyperglycaemic. In muscle it has the effect of increasing lactate production, and lactate is a substrate for gluconeogenesis in both liver and muscle. A fall in blood glucose level produces an increased level of adrenalin in the blood. Adrenalin also inhibits the action of the third principal hormone, insulin.

3 **Insulin** has a number of effects, all of which tend to *lower* the blood glucose level: in fact, it is the only *hypo*glycaemic hormone. Its main effect is to promote the transfer of glucose out of the blood and into cells. One of the ways that this comes about is that insulin enhances the activity of some of the enzymes involved in glycolysis. This increases the demand in the cells for glucose, and so reduces the blood glucose level.

Sufferers from **diabetes** have low levels of insulin in their blood, or insulin may be absent. As a result, their blood glucose levels will be high, but the level of glucose in the cells will be low. Diabetes is treated by controlling the diet and, often, by injecting insulin. Injections have to be repeated daily, since insulin is rapidly degraded in the body—half of it being destroyed within about 10–15 minutes. As you should remember from Unit 22, Section 3.4, insulin is a protein that is destroyed by proteolytic (protein-destroying) enzymes, so it cannot be taken by mouth because it would be broken down by enzymes in the intestine before it could diffuse through into the bloodstream. Injections of insulin cannot produce a perfect match between blood glucose levels and blood insulin levels. Thus, even though insulin treatment is very effective, it is still possible for the blood glucose level to rise or fall too much. As a result diabetics need to monitor their blood glucose levels regularly. One method available to them is to use colour-indicating strips of the type shown in use in the TV programme. The strips are sensitive to glucose in a blood droplet, and change colour. The colour gives an accurate measure of glucose concentration, which can be read directly using a cheap test instrument (also shown in the TV programme).

Hyperglycaemia can be recognized by an increased feeling of thirst. Hypoglycaemia can be recognized because the adrenalin level in the blood rises, and adrenalin has a number of other recognizable effects on the body, producing nervousness, weakness, anxiety, increased heart rate, and headache.

SUMMARY OF SECTION 5

1 The bloodstream provides glucose as a metabolic substrate for cells.

2 Cells in the brain and nervous system can utilize only glucose as a source of energy. For them, low blood glucose levels are harmful.

3 A number of mechanisms are utilized to maintain blood glucose at a safe level, even during starvation. Glycogen stores are converted to glucose (glycogenolysis), and glucose is synthesized from a variety of substrates (gluconeogenesis). These changes occur mainly in the liver. Muscles catabolize fats, thus sparing glucose for brain tissue.

HOMEOSTASIS

REFERENCE LEVEL

RECEPTOR

SIGNAL

MONITOR

EFFECTOR

NEGATIVE FEEDBACK

POSITIVE FEEDBACK

4   A hormone is a molecule that is synthesized by one group of cells and exerts its effect upon another group—its target cells.

5   Some hormones initiate glucose synthesis and glycogen breakdown, thus raising blood glucose level. The two key hormones involved are glucagon and adrenalin.

6   In contrast, insulin is a hormone that lowers the blood glucose level by promoting metabolism in the cells.

SAQ 6   What would you expect to be the consequences of an injection of too much insulin into a diabetic person? How could the person cope with the consequences?

SAQ 7   What would have happened to the lactate levels produced in your blood after the stepping exercise? Think back to the experiment in Section 3.3.

6 CONTROL MECHANISMS

In the preceding Sections, you have seen how oxygen and glucose are supplied to cells, how water and waste compounds are removed, and how heat is transported. In each Section there has been a hint that all these processes are under some form of control. This is indeed the case and, because the principles of control are common to all biological systems, it is sensible to devote a separate section to the subject. As well as describing some of the common factors of control mechanisms, we look at a number of examples that bear upon the themes of this Unit.

The physiological control mechanisms in organisms keep order and prevent the onset of chaos. They maintain stability so that all the processes going on in the organism proceed at the optimum rate for the current circumstances. There is not just a single level of activity to be maintained, though. The blood flow required for a human at rest is different from the flow required by the same human swimming steadily across the Channel. The regulation of physiological function to maintain a particular stable state is called **homeostasis** (meaning 'staying the same').

Can you think of an example (biological or otherwise) of a regulated process, and an example of an unregulated one?

There are many examples that you might have suggested of a regulated process, but a good one is the thermostatic control of heating systems in houses, or the cooling system in refrigerators, cars, etc. There are fewer common examples of unregulated processes. An explosion is perhaps the most familiar—you can't stop it or alter the rate once it has started!

In Figure 16, you can see how (at its simplest) a room thermostat controls a domestic heating system to produce a stable room temperature. This type of diagram is called a flow diagram, and similar ones are often used to describe the arrangement of physiological control systems. Many of the features of artificial systems, such as this central heating layout, are paralleled in biological regulation. It is instructive, therefore, to look for the *principles of regulation* in familiar manufactured systems and then to apply them to organisms. You should remember, however, that no analogy is quite perfect.

In the system in Figure 16, the aim of the control is to achieve a pre-set room temperature of 18 °C. Because it is pre-set, 18 °C is called the **reference level**. The thermostat senses the room temperature and, as it receives information about temperature, it can be termed a temperature **receptor**. When the temperature falls below the reference level, the receptor sends a **signal** to a control unit (the **monitor**), and that sends another signal to a pump and boiler (the **effector**) that circulates hot water through the radiator. As the radiators release heat into the room, the temperature increase

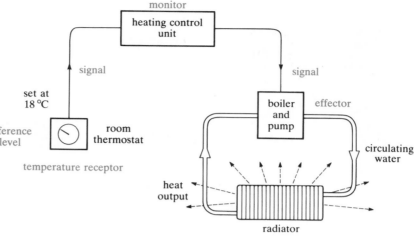

FIGURE 16 This is a simplified diagram of a central heating system (one room, one radiator). The terms in red are the functions of the various parts, and these terms can be applied unchanged to physiological systems. The reference level in this Figure is the temperature selected as a comfortable one by the occupant of the room: 18 °C.

is sensed by the thermostat. Via signals to the monitor and thence to the effector, heat production is switched off. Thus temperature is *controlled* at about the reference level.

A regulatory device in which a signal registering a temperature *increase* causes a change that *halts* (or *negates*) the temperature increase is said to depend on **negative feedback**—'feedback' because information is fed back to the effector; 'negative' because the activity of the effector is, when the reference point is reached, eliminated (negated) by the very effect it produces. In later parts of this Section, you will come across many examples of homeostasis—and *all* of them depend on negative feedback.

Positive feedback has no part—indeed, can have no part—in any homeostatic system. The following short discussion is included simply so that this potentially confusing term is made clear.

☐ If *negative* feedback involves switching off an effector as a consequence of the change produced by the effector, what would *positive* feedback do?

■ The change produced by the effector would cause the effector to produce yet more change in the same direction. This is the very reverse of control—an explosion is a good non-biological example.

There are a few biological examples of positive feedback, all connected with processes that need to go rapidly and effectively to total completion. One such is the process of birth. The baby's head stretches the vagina as the contractions of the womb force it downwards. This distends the vagina, and the muscles respond to the stretching by *increasing* the number and strength of their contractions. This leads to more stretching, increased contraction, more push on the baby, and birth!

Let us return to negative feedback—as noted earlier, only this is involved in homeostatic systems. Six important terms have been introduced: receptor, signal, monitor, reference level, effector and negative feedback.

ITQ 7 Using only these six terms, complete the blanks in the following passage—in order to convince yourself that you understand their proper usage in the context of a control system.

In the heating system in Figure 16, a change in temperature is detected by the thermostat. The latter is termed the ...*receptor*.......... because it receives information about the temperature of the room. In this particular control system, the thermostat also contains the pre-set ...*reference*... ...*level*.... A ...*signal*.... passes from this point to the ...*monitor*....... This compares the incoming information with its internal instructions and, as a consequence, sends a ...*signal*...... to the ...*effector*.. This is switched on, so heating the room. Eventually the

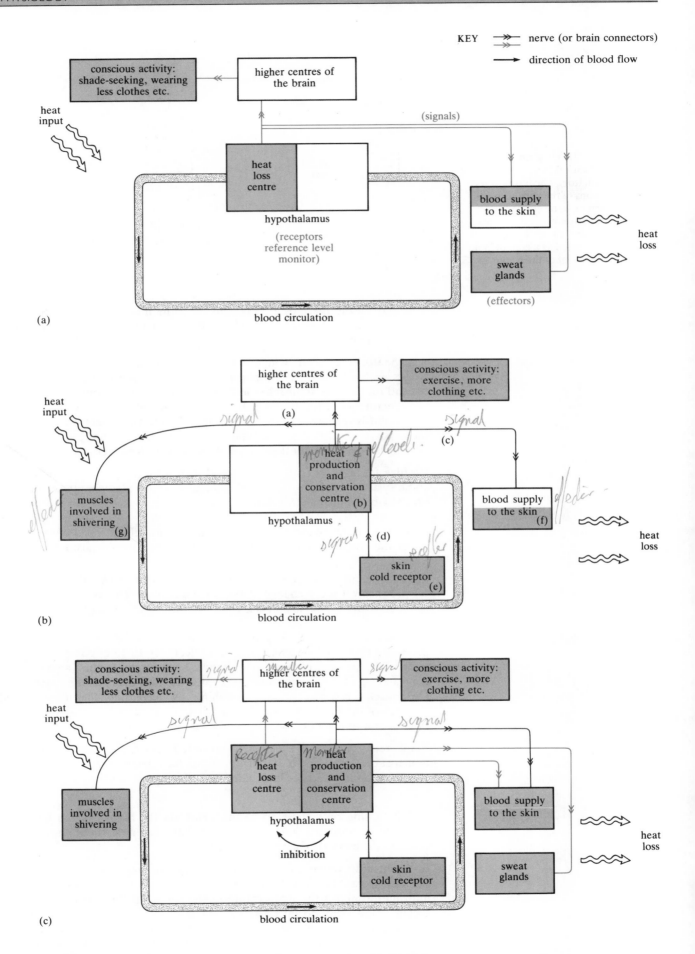

FIGURE 17   The thermoregulatory system in humans. (a) The cooling part of the system. Double arrows denote signals. (b) The heating and heat conservation part of the system. The bracketed letters refer to ITQ 8. (c) The two parts of the system combined. Note that when one centre in the hypothalamus is active, the other is inhibited, and vice versa.

HYPOTHALAMUS

temperature increases to the point at which the ....
.... is exceeded. When this happens, the .... is
switched off via the control system, so preventing any further rise. This is an
example of .... feedback.

Let us turn to a biological control system and apply these terms. In Section
4.3 it was noted that, in birds and mammals, regulatory systems maintain
the inner temperature very close to the reference level for each species—at
around 37 °C in humans and many other mammals, a little higher for many
birds. The thermoregulatory system is more complicated than the central
heating system shown in Figure 16. This is because, depending on
environmental conditions, the system has either to act as a *cooler* (keeping
the temperature down) or as a *heating system* (keeping the temperature up).

Look at Figure 17. The first part of this, Figure 17a, is the cooling part, and
it covers items that should be familiar to you from Section 4.3. The reference level is contained within the monitor—a small structure at the base of
the brain called the **hypothalamus** (see Figure 18). The tissue of this organ is
well supplied with blood from part of the systemic circulation, and has
within it temperature receptors that measure blood temperature. When this
rises above the reference level, impulses in nerves leaving the monitor send
a signal to the effectors. These are the arterioles of the skin (dilation of them
permits quantities of blood to travel near to the skin surface) and the sweat
glands (production of sweat, which then evaporates, aids heat loss). Thus,
through the activity of these effectors, heat is lost. The operation of negative
feedback is plain to see—the nerve impulse signalling an increase in temperature brings about a change that *negates* that increase. Figure 17a shows
the role played by each component. The *heat loss centre*, as this part of the
hypothalamus is termed, also passes information about temperature to
higher centres of the brain—and in turn initiates voluntary behaviour such
as drinking, seeking shade, removing clothing and so on.

Now look at Figure 17b. This deals with the heat production and conservation part of the system. Once again, the hypothalamus contains the reference level and monitor—but this time a different part, called the *heat
conservation and production centre*, is involved. The temperature of the
blood entering this part of the hypothalamus may have some effect, but it is
the cold temperature receptors in the skin that are of most significance.
These send signals, via nerves, to the monitor where detected skin temperature is compared with the reference level. If the temperature is lower
than this reference, nerve impulses signal the effectors to conserve heat (skin
arterioles which contract, diminishing supply to the skin surface) and to
generate heat (the muscles involved in shivering). Once again, information
passed by the hypothalamus to the higher centres of the brain is very
important, for certain voluntary activity such as vigorous exercise and
putting on more clothing are more effective at maintaining body temperature than shivering.

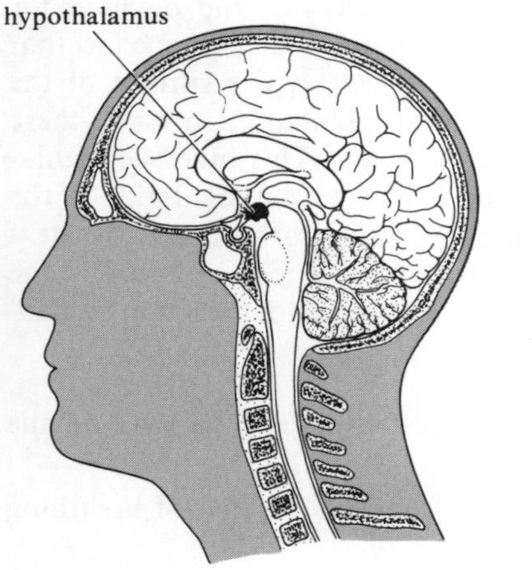

Figure 17c shows the two subsystems combined—giving the overall,
complex, system of thermoregulation. Try the following ITQ to check that
you are familiar with the features of this kind of homeostatic system: you
will meet others in later parts of this Unit and it is important to feel con-
fident about the standard components.

hypothalamus

FIGURE 18   A human brain, showing
the position of the hypothalamus.

ITQ **8**   Assign one or more of the terms, *receptor*, *reference level*, *monitor*,
effector and *signal* to the letters (a) to (g) in Figure 17b, so as to describe
their role in this subsystem of the thermoregulation system in humans.

6.1 CONTROL OF BLOOD GLUCOSE LEVEL

The purpose of this brief Section is to link—in outline only—the general
features of homeostasis that we have just discussed to the regulation of
blood glucose. As you know from Section 5.4, the level of blood glucose is
regulated through the action of the hormones insulin, glucagon and adrenalin. Thus, a significant difference between this regulatory system and that

PANCREAS

MEDULLA (OF BRAIN)

PONS

CEREBRAL CORTEX

CHEMORECEPTOR

CEREBROSPINAL FLUID

for temperature, is that the signalling is achieved through the circulation of *hormones* rather than by the transmission of *nerve impulses*. Otherwise, as you will shortly see, the system contains the familiar components of homeostasis and the expected operation of a negative feedback system. In the next paragraph we shall simplify the topic by considering only one hormone: insulin.

Insulin is, as has been said, the signal. It is secreted by particular cells (B cells) of an organ located near the liver called the **pancreas**, and, as you would expect, the amount of insulin secreted into blood passing through it is markedly altered by the level of glucose in that blood.

□ Given (from Section 5.4) that insulin brings about a *fall* in blood glucose level, would you expect the pancreas to secrete more insulin or less insulin when blood glucose increases?

■ To achieve homeostasis, more insulin must be secreted when blood glucose is raised.

The pancreas contains the glucose receptors and the reference level. By responding to the detected glucose level, it also acts as the monitor. The effectors are all tissues in which the uptake of glucose is stimulated by the insulin, with liver tissue having a major role. This is, as you may have realized from earlier Sections, only part of the system. A further set of *hyperglycaemic hormones* (including glucagon and adrenalin) are involved in *raising* blood glucose when it falls below the reference level. However, in these much simplified terms, you should be able to see how blood glucose level is regulated by a system that depends on the negative feedback of information received in the pancreas, transmitted by a hormone and acted upon by tissues.

The importance and effectiveness of the system is brought out in the details of the TV programme. That programme also considers the role of breathing and heart rate in metabolism, and it is to the regulation of those features that we now turn.

6.2 CONTROL OF BREATHING

As you should have realized by now, exercise increases the demand for oxygen and, at the same time, it generates more CO_2. This means that there must be an increased exchange of both gases at the surface of the lungs and, also, an increase in the rate of blood circulation to move these gases from lungs to tissues and from tissues to lungs. This involves regulation of *breathing* and of *cardiac output*—and, of course, the regulation of the two must be closely linked. This Section considers breathing and the next (Section 6.3) deals with cardiac output. A feature of both stories is the detection and regulation of carbon dioxide in blood to preserve homeostasis.

□ What effect would you expect a raised blood CO_2 level to have on the rate of breathing and the heart rate?

■ You should expect a raised CO_2 level to increase the rate of breathing and to increase cardiac output.

□ In theoretical terms, what alternative (or supplementary) method of control could also be effective?

■ Control could be achieved through blood oxygen levels. This time, a high level of blood oxygen should decrease breathing rate and decrease cardiac output.

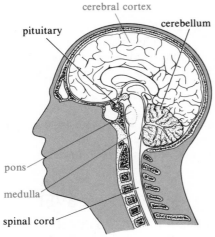

FIGURE 19 A human brain. The areas responsible for the control of breathing are lettered in red.

Breathing in humans is a rhythmical process. An area of the brain called the **medulla** (Figure 19) contains a rhythm generator. This provides the basic pattern of breathing, and it runs continuously, providing a signal to start inspiration (that is, breathing in). A second signal from a nearby part of the brain called the **pons** starts expiration (breathing out) by inhibiting the inspiration signal. The two form part of the 'Hering–Breuer reflex' (called after the two men who discovered it in 1868). As we shall see, variation in the relative timing of these two signals provides a means of control of breathing. Receptors in the lung walls detect how much the lungs have been inflated and, at a certain point, they trigger signals that stop the contraction of the respiratory muscles. This is another example of a feedback loop (involving, this time, signals in nerves and not via hormones).

But, how is the basic 'in-and-out' pattern of the Hering–Breuer reflex modulated, that is, how is it varied according to the needs of the body to obtain oxygen or eliminate CO_2? A limited amount of voluntary control is possible. People preparing to swim underwater can choose to breathe hard and so decrease the CO_2 level in their blood before starting—a process called hyperventilation. Similarly, once underwater the breath can be held at will for a short time. This voluntary control involves the higher centres of the brain in the **cerebral cortex**. But voluntary control is of relatively minor significance. More important is that the 'in-and-out' pattern adjusts automatically to achieve necessary gas exchange. The surfacing and now air-hungry diver does not have to *think* to breathe hard: he just does. How is this achieved?

In Equation 1 (Section 2) you saw that exercise uses oxygen and produces CO_2. In Equation 4 (Section 4.1) you saw that dissolved CO_2 leads to the production of H^+ ions and hence a decrease in pH. That decrease in pH is the basis on which receptors for carbon dioxide or **chemoreceptors** (so called because they respond to chemical signals) work. These receptors are located in the medulla of the brain (see Figures 19 and 20). Though the receptors are not in direct contact with blood, CO_2 diffuses from plasma into the fluid bathing the brain—the **cerebrospinal fluid**. Here H^+ ions are produced as described above. When the receptors detect an increase in H^+ concentration, a signal of nerve impulses reaches the effectors—in this case, the respiratory muscles—and an increased breathing rate results. Thus, *high* blood CO_2 levels produce an increase in the rate of breathing which results in a subsequent *lowering* of blood CO_2 levels. This is another example of negative feedback.

The system described above is complicated by a number of features. In particular, there is a further set of chemoreceptors, known as peripheral chemoreceptors, in the large arteries that carry oxygenated blood away from the heart (Figure 20). These differ from the receptors in the medulla in that they detect changes in *oxygen concentration* as well as in CO_2 concentration. For example, if the oxygen level falls, signals are sent to the brain which responds by increasing the rate of contraction of the respiratory muscles, and an increase in breathing rate occurs. In fact, these peripheral receptors are much more sensitive to changes in the level of CO_2 than to changes in the level of oxygen—and the oxygen level at the receptors would have to fall nearly to the level of oxygen in venous blood before they would initiate a signal.

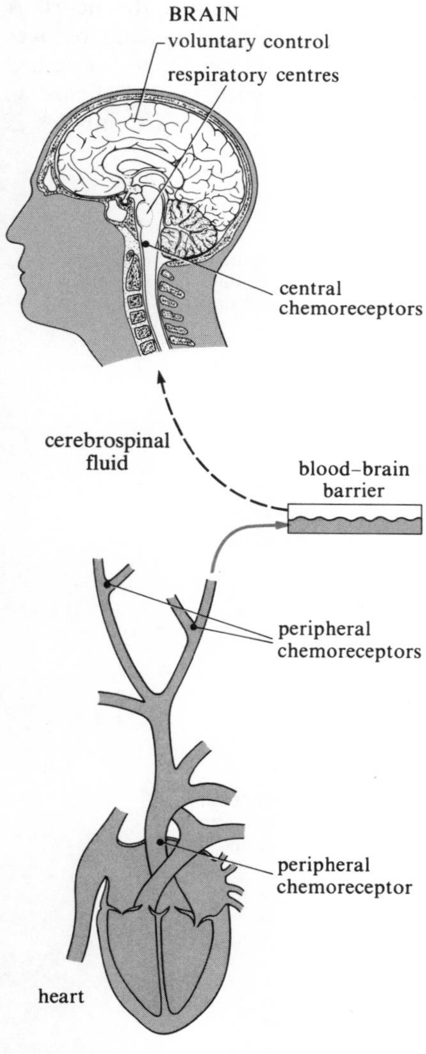

6.3 NERVOUS CONTROL OF HEART BEAT

The need for effective control of cardiac output is very apparent if you think back to Sam, after his jog, in the TV programme. The blood *in the lungs* will be freshly loaded with oxygen and swept clear of CO_2. But to make use of these gas exchanges, there must be rapid circulation of blood to the tissues of the body where oxygen is needed, and respiratory CO_2 awaits removal. How is this achieved? Once again, we shall be looking for effectors, receptors and an intervening monitor and reference level.

Changes in cardiac output are primarily produced by alterations in the rate of contraction and the stroke volume of the heart. Cardiac output is also influenced by the contraction or dilation of the arterioles and arteries, but this discussion will focus on the heart as an effector.

BRAIN
voluntary control
respiratory centres

central
chemoreceptors

cerebrospinal
fluid

blood–brain
barrier

peripheral
chemoreceptors

peripheral
chemoreceptor

heart

FIGURE 20 The basic components of the respiratory control system in humans.

In breathing, there is a basic 'in-and-out' rhythm that is modulated according to need. There is a similar modulation of the rhythm of the heart. A totally excised heart—that is, one cut out of the body—will continue beating if it is bathed with the right kind of saline solution. Within the heart (in ways not discussed here), special fibres coordinate movements of the two atria and two ventricles in the standard sequence of muscular pumping. Modulation of that rhythm is achieved, as we shall see, by two distinct kinds of nerves.

Several of the control systems so far described depend on the transmission of information by nerve impulses. Information is coded in nerves in an electrical form. A single nerve cell—a **neuron**—carries electrical pulses of identical size and duration. It can be the time interval between pulses, or the patterning of the pulses or, indeed the presence or absence of pulses, that encodes information. Nerves that carry information from receptor to the monitor (in the brain) are termed **sensory nerves**. Those that travel from the brain are—if the effector is a muscle—termed **motor nerves**. As noted above, the mammalian heart exhibits a complexity that we have not met before: it is supplied by two kinds of motor nerve—one that stimulates it (part of the **sympathetic nervous system**) and one that inhibits it (part of the **parasympathetic nervous system**). The advantage of one system acting *antagonistically* to the other is that large changes in rate can be produced rapidly. For example, a small change in activity in each of the nerves will produce a large change in rate. A decrease in parasympathetic impulses increases heart rate and an increase in sympathetic activity also produces an increase in heart rate. (The 'beta-blockers' that you read about in Units 17–18 block the effect of the sympathetic nerves supplying the heart. A common drug, propranolol, by blocking the sympathetic system, reduces the heart rate.) The medulla (which you met before when we discussed control of breathing in Section 6.2) is also concerned with control of cardiac output. A simple representation of the nerve supply to heart muscles is shown in Figure 21.

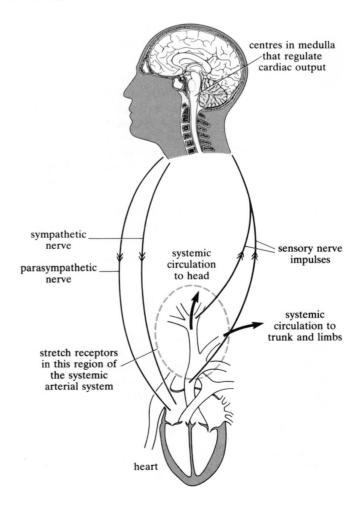

FIGURE 21 A simple representation of the nerve supply to the heart.

What kind of stimulus is detected in this system? You might reasonably expect raised CO_2 or lowered O_2 to have a stimulatory effect—both would then cause an increase in the heart rate during exercise. There is some evidence that chemoreceptors in the large arteries leaving the heart may play a minor part in the direct regulation of cardiac output. There is rather more evidence, however, that chemoreception of CO_2 has an indirect effect on the circulation by influencing the contraction or dilation of arteries and arterioles. Much more significant in direct heart beat regulation is the detection of *blood pressure*. In the aorta (the main artery leaving the heart carrying the systemic circulation, shown in Plate 9) and in the arteries leading to the head, there are special **stretch receptors** that detect changes in blood pressure.

☐ In terms of homeostasis of blood pressure, would you expect a signal from stretch receptors (indicating rising pressure) to lead, via the monitor in the medulla, to sympathetic or parasympathetic stimulation of the heart?

■ Parasympathetic—leading to decreased heart rate, hence lowered pressure.

Thus, as described in this simplified outline, we have a homeostatic system for blood pressure. This time it depends on detection of pressure, modulation via a monitor (containing a reference level) in the medulla, and affected by the activity of the heart muscles. It relates easily to the metabolic needs of exercise. As noted earlier, CO_2 brings about dilation of the tissue arterioles, giving plenty of 'local blood' to supply oxygen and remove carbon dioxide. This dilation has the effect, of course, of lowering resistance to blood flow and so lowering blood pressure. And this, in turn is detected by the pressure receptors and so on.

Blood pressure homeostasis has important links with other control systems that you have already met. Various changes can occur *very rapidly* in the diameters of arterioles and arteries and have very marked effects on blood pressure—to which the heart must respond. For example, when the body is chilled, the blood supply to the capillaries in the skin is reduced. If blood is thus excluded from a significant proportion of the circulatory system, it is plain that, since the volume of blood is fixed, the pressure in the rest of the system will rise drastically unless the rate of heart beat is sharply reduced. This is achieved through the pressure homeostatic system: as pressure rises, stretch receptors are triggered, impulses pass down the parasympathetic nerves, and the heart rate slows.

We can usefully conclude this discussion with another foray into comparative physiology. Much of the early work on heart function was done on isolated frog hearts and, consequently, a good deal is known about the function of this organ. Although the frog heart resembles the mammalian heart in many ways, it has only one ventricle. The consequence of this is that oxygenated and deoxygenated blood mix in the ventricle. This may strike you as inefficient, but, as you will see, it is quite the reverse.

Think where frogs live. Their habitat is very wet. Because their skin is both thin and wet, oxygen can diffuse directly through to the bloodstream. Thus, the lung is not the only source of oxygen and, when the frog is underwater, the oxygen that the frog needs will come from the surrounding water via the skin. The advantage of having only one ventricle is now apparent. Blood from the skin that is rich in oxygen *can go directly to the tissues*. If the frog had a double circulation like that in mammals, the blood from the skin, already rich in oxygen, would then pass through the lungs for no purpose. As it is, the arrangement is ideal for the circumstances in which the frog lives.

Experiments with frogs have also provided further insights into heart function—as we shall show in Section 6.4.

6.4 HORMONAL CONTROL OF HEART BEAT

In an early physiological experiment, two frog hearts were set up in isolation (Figure 22). The only link between them was the circulating fluid. When the nerve to the first heart was stimulated by a mild electric current, the rate of beating altered, as you would expect. A much more surprising result was that the rate of the second heart also altered. The conclusion drawn was that there was chemical communication between the two hearts. Other experiments supported this conclusion, and eliminated other explanations, for example that the electrical signal passed through the circulating fluid. Thus, it was clear that one should look for a role for *hormones* in beat rate regulation.

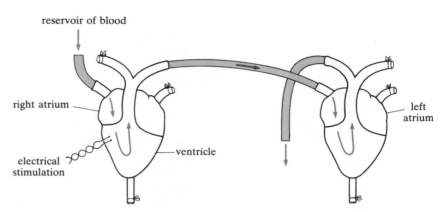

FIGURE 22 An early experiment in which two isolated frog hearts were connected together by tubing carrying a solution resembling blood. It demonstrated that, if one heart was stimulated electrically, a chemical in the fluid carried the signal for contraction from one heart to the other. The direction of movement of the solution is shown by the red arrows. Note that in the frog heart there is only one ventricle.

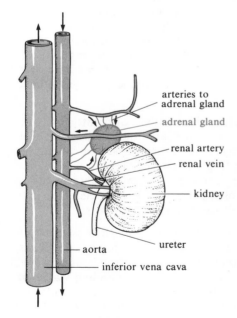

FIGURE 23 The position of the adrenal glands and the blood vessels supplying them, in a human.

You have already met the hormone adrenalin in Section 5.4. It is produced in the **adrenal glands**, two small pea-shaped organs situated close to the kidneys or directly attached to them (Figure 23). There are two layers of tissue in the adrenal glands: the outer **cortex** and the inner medulla. The hormone adrenalin can be extracted from the medulla, and when it is injected into animals or humans it produces a wide variety of effects: an increase in the rate of breathing, an increase in the heart rate, and increased glucose release from the liver. In addition, there is an increase in resistance to blood flow in the skin, caused by the reduction of blood flow to the skin capillaries, leading to the typical paleness of shock. Also, there is, in humans, a feeling of anxiety. All these physiological responses occur also when the body is subjected to sudden stress, such as fright.

When the brain is stimulated by stress, a signal is sent via the sympathetic nervous system to the adrenal glands. Adrenalin is stored in the tissue of the glands in the form of inert granules, and the signal causes the start of release of active hormone into the bloodstream. When the hormone is in the bloodstream, it passes through the heart, and also enters the heart's own blood supply—the coronary blood vessels which supply the heart muscle with oxygen, glucose, etc. (Figure 9b). Thus adrenalin is delivered directly to its site of action—the heart muscle. Here, it mimics the action of the sympathetic nervous system.

What is its effect on beat rate?

It causes faster and stronger contraction of the muscle, by increasing both heart rate and stroke volume, and cardiac output is increased, initially overriding the nervous control. When the stress is passed, and adrenalin release has ceased, the levels of adrenalin in the blood fall. The fall is due to the action of enzymes that continually catalyse the breakdown of adrenalin in blood and tissues, to prevent it from continuing to stimulate the body after the need for it has passed.

ITQ 9 Is the release of adrenalin under conditions of stress a homeostatic response? Give reasons for your answer.

From the answer to ITQ 9, it is clear that adrenalin is quite unlike a homeostatic hormonal such as insulin. Adrenalin is released in response to stress, and it has a wide range of physiological effects. It is possible to determine experimentally the types of stress that produce adrenalin release, and it is also possible to measure how much adrenalin is released in these varying conditions. The blood test has to be quite sensitive since an injection of a very small quantity—about $0.2\,\mu g\,l^{-1}$ of adrenalin—produces quite a large heart rate response. As a result of such measurements, we know that adrenalin is released in response to:

1 physical exertion
2 exposure to cold
3 reduction in blood pressure
4 reduction in blood flow to the brain
5 hypoglycaemia
6 anaesthetic drugs
7 emotional states such as fright

All the physiological effects of adrenalin that we have mentioned tend to counteract the seven kinds of stress listed above.

SUMMARY OF SECTION 6

1 The survival of organisms depends upon efficient coordination of physiological processes.

2 Homeostatic mechanisms maintain the organism in an appropriate state: they act to restore stability by negative feedback.

3 Information about the state of the organism is acquired by receptors and passed to effectors.

4 In mammals, the oxygen level of the blood is maintained by a combination of adjustment of blood flow and breathing.

5 Information about the gas content of the blood is acquired by central and peripheral chemoreceptors.

6 Breathing rate and heart rate have natural rhythms that are modulated by the brain on the basis of information received from receptors.

7 The heart receives signals from both the sympathetic and the parasympathetic nervous systems. The signals act antagonistically to produce a high degree of control of heart rate, and a rapid response.

8 Adrenalin, released from the adrenal glands near the kidney, stimulates the heart to increase rate and stroke volume. It also generally increases the state of preparedness of the body for rapid action.

SAQ 8 Describe the possible physiological consequences of going swimming off Brighton beach on Christmas Day, and then coming ashore and swallowing a large brandy (or two). (*Hint* Think about what would happen to the blood vessels in the skin, since one of the actions of alcohol is to dilate blood vessels.)

SAQ 9 Figure 24 shows the relation between the rate of heat loss by sweating and body temperature for a woman with a slight fever (dotted line) and a woman in normal health (dashed line), under controlled conditions. Body temperature has been measured by monitoring the temperature at the carotid artery in the neck. Which *one* of the following deductions can reasonably be made from the graph?

(a) The fever causes the small capillaries in the skin to narrow in diameter.
(b) The fever alters the activity of the sweat glands so that they secrete more sweat.

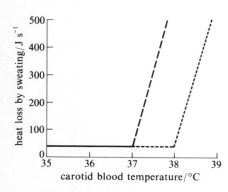

FIGURE 24 Figure for SAQ 9.

(c) The fever alters the temperature at which the hypothalamus initiates sweating.

(d) The effect of the fever is to reduce the heart rate, and so reduce the blood flow through the skin.

SAQ 10   How do the differences in the structure of the heart between mammals and frogs relate to the supply of oxygen to the tissues?

7 CONCLUSION

The preceding pages have considered the regulation of body temperature, blood glucose level, breathing, and cardiac output. In the last of these, the effect of adrenalin in stimulating the heart to sudden high levels of activity was non-homeostatic. All the other processes involve negative feedback and hence homeostasis. In all of them, a changing level of some attribute (glucose level, temperature) is detected by receptors which, after comparison with some reference level in the monitor, leads to an alteration in effector activity in the direction of countering the perceived change. These are common features in all homeostatic systems. Apart from differences in detail, the only major way in which one homeostatic system may differ from another is in the nature of the signal—which may be hormonal (as in glucose regulation) or nervous (as in temperature regulation).

In this Unit we have looked at a number of physiological systems in animals, and considered their function as part of the whole organism. Although we have described a very varied group of systems, they all have the same role: that of maintaining the internal environment. They act to keep physiological and biochemical events within a tolerable range.

This is not a novel way of looking at the natural world; it was established by Claude Bernard, a French physiologist, in the 19th century (Plate 11). He formulated his ideas during a study of the role of the liver as a glycogen store. So although he did not himself invent the term homeostasis, he is rightly remembered as the originator of the homeostatic systems approach to the study of physiology—the approach we have followed throughout this Unit.

Although, working in the 19th century, Bernard could not have known it, a great many physiological processes are influenced by enzymes and other proteins such as haemoglobin, insulin and many more. This leads us back to a matter of great importance—the link between genes, metabolic proteins and, in turn, to the overall physiology of an organism. That link, a closer exploration of 'DNA makes RNA makes protein', is the subject of Unit 24.

OBJECTIVES FOR UNIT 23

After you have worked through this Unit, you should be able to:

1 Explain the meaning of, and use correctly, all the terms flagged in the text.

2 Describe the supply of oxygen to cells in animals and recognize the limitations on size imposed by the lack of a circulatory system. (*SAQs 1 and 2*)

3 Describe the supply of oxygen and respiratory substrates to the cells in mammalian tissues, and the removal of waste products. (*ITQs 1–4; SAQ 4*)

4 Describe the circulation of blood through the heart and lungs of a mammal and distinguish between the structure and function of veins and arteries. (*ITQ 5; SAQ 3*)

5 Explain the role of blood cells in the transport of dissolved gases. (*SAQ 5*)

6 Outline the effects of diabetes, and explain how blood sugar levels can be controlled in this disease. (*SAQ 6*)

7 Distinguish in general terms between amphibian and mammalian circulatory systems. (*SAQ 9*)

8 Identify the key features of control mechanisms and explain the difference between homeostatic and non-homeostatic mechanisms. (*ITQ 6–8; SAQ 10*)

9 Give an account of the control mechanisms involved in maintaining homeostasis in the following mammalian systems:

(a) thermoregulation system (*ITQs 7 and 8*)
(b) glucose supply (*SAQ 7*)
(c) heart and circulatory system (*SAQ 8*)

FURTHER READING

For an introduction to comparative animal physiology, we suggest that you read:

Wood, D. W. (1983) *Principles of Animal Physiology*, Edward Arnold.

Human physiology is covered very well, though at a higher level than in this Unit, in a series of books called *Physiological Principles in Medicine*. (The series is still being expanded.) Particularly relevant to this Unit are:

Sandford, P. A. (1982) *Digestive System Physiology*, Edward Arnold.

Widdicombe, J. and Davies, A. (1983) *Respiratory Physiology*, Edward Arnold.

Hardy, R. N. (1982) *Endocrine Physiology*, Edward Arnold.

For a very well illustrated textbook that covers most of the biology in S102 in detail, we recommend:

Starr, C. and Taggart, R. (1987) *Biology, The Unity and Diversity of Life*, Wadsworth Publishing Co.

ITQ ANSWERS AND COMMENTS

ITQ 1 45 beats min^{-1}. In one second there would be $30/40 = 0.75$ beats. So in 60 seconds there would be 60×0.75 beats, so the heart rate is 45 beats min^{-1}.

ITQ 2 The pulse is a repetitive event consisting of the pulse you feel plus the space between the pulses. To get thirty complete cycles of pulse and 'space' you need to count from the instant you feel pulse 1 to the instant you feel pulse 31. You then have thirty pulses and thirty spaces.

ITQ 3 The stroke volume was about 150 cm^3. Using Equation 2, the calculation is:

$$\text{stroke volume} = \frac{\text{cardiac output}}{\text{heart rate}}$$
$$= \frac{25 \text{ litres min}^{-1} \times 1\,000 \text{ cm}^3}{170 \text{ beats min}^{-1}}$$
$$\approx 150 \text{ cm}^3$$

Athletes train hard and develop powerful muscles. The training also affects the heart muscle, and athletes can achieve the same cardiac output as an untrained person, but with a slower heart rate. This is why the figures in this example differ from those given in the text for a relatively fit person.

ITQ 4 (a) The dye circulates through the bloodstream and is gradually diluted. It is not instantly dispersed throughout the blood. So the first peak represents the dye passing the sample point during the first complete circulation. The level falls, only to rise again during the second circulation. The second peak would be lower as the dye is by then more dispersed in the blood.

(b) The peak in the exercise curve occurs earlier because blood is circulating faster and therefore the dye travels round the blood system and reaches point S more quickly. During exercise, heart rate and stroke volume increase.

ITQ 5 About 4.9 litres min^{-1}. You were told that the mean dye concentration was 1.6 mg l^{-1}. Since 5 mg was injected, the volume of blood that contained the dye was $5/1.6 = 3.13$ litres. Extending the slope of the resting curve to the horizontal axis shows that the dye takes 38.5 seconds to pass through the heart once. So 3.13 litres circulates in 38.5 s. It follows that $(3.13/38.5) \times 60$ litres circulates in one minute. This is about 4.9 litres min^{-1}.

ITQ 6 The human body loses water through several main routes:

(a) During breathing water is lost by evaporation from the linings of the nose, lungs, and mouth.

(b) Water is lost via the skin by sweating.

(c) The body discards waste, and loses water as it does so. Urination may be a way of getting rid of excess water, but urine also has the function of removing nitrogen from the body.

ITQ 7 The completed passage should read as follows:

In the heating system in Figure 16, a change in temperature is detected by the thermostat. The latter is termed the *receptor* because it receives information about the temperature of the room. In this particular control system, the thermostat also contains the pre-set *reference level*. A *signal* passes from this point to the *monitor*. This compares the incoming information with its internal instructions, and, as a consequence, sends a *signal* to the *effector*. This is switched on, so heating the room. Eventually the temperature increases to the point at which the *reference level* is exceeded. When this happens, the *effector* is switched off via the control system, so preventing any further rise. This is an example of *negative* feedback.

ITQ 8 The labelled parts of the regulatory subsystem shown in Figure 17b are:

(a) signal (nerve impulse);
(b) monitor and reference level;
(c) signal (nerve impulse);
(d) signal (nerve impulse);
(e) receptor;
(f) effector;
(g) effector.

ITQ 9 The release of adrenalin in response to stress is not a homeostatic response. In this situation a temporary increase in the level of circulating adrenalin leads to a number of temporary adjustments of the body's physiology, which all contribute to overcoming stress, or help survival in an emergency. The action of adrenalin is to produce an unstable state rapidly, but temporarily. There is a subsequent restoration of homeostasis by other means.

SAQ ANSWERS AND COMMENTS

SAQ 1 (a) has the larger concentration gradient. In both (a) and (b) the cells are the same. So the concentration difference between each cell and the pondwater is the same. However, the distances are different. The greater the distance from the pondwater, the smaller the concentration gradient. So (a) has the larger concentration gradient.

SAQ 2 (a) will have the larger diffusion rate. Both cells are the same distance from the pondwater, but that in (a) is metabolizing much faster than that in (b), which has very few mitochondria. Therefore the oxygen concentration difference will be greater in (a), the concentration gradient will be larger and so the diffusion rate will be greater.

SAQ 3 (b) and (d) are true.

(a) is false because the pulmonary artery carries blood to the lung. This blood has been carried to the heart from the tissues and, having given up oxygen, it has collected carbon dioxide to be disposed of.

(b) is true because most veins bring blood from tissues, where oxygen will have been used, back to the heart. An exception is the pulmonary vein, which carries oxygen-rich blood.

(c) is false because all blood has to pass through both heart and lungs.

(d) is true because the two routes through the heart are independent. There is a true double circulation.

SAQ 4 In Unit 22 you saw that it was possible to generate ATP by glycolysis in the absence of oxygen. The stepping exercise in the experiment should have been sufficiently strenuous to cause you or your assistant to generate ATP from anaerobic respiration. One of the consequences of exercise is a build-up of lactate—the oxygen debt (Unit 22, Section 6.4). The oxygen required to pay off this debt comes from the increased cardiac output being maintained after exercise, only returning to normal when the debt is paid off. Lactate accumulation makes muscles feel tired.

SAQ 5 It is advantageous for blood to have a low viscosity because it travels through vessels of very narrow diameter. The thicker blood is, the more pressure is required to force it through a narrow tube of a given diameter and the greater the resulting load on the heart. Imagine the difference between forcing water out of a syringe needle, and forcing treacle out of the same syringe. The treacle would require more pressure—indeed, you might crack the syringe.

SAQ 6 Injection of too much insulin would promote glucose transfer out of the blood into cells. The blood glucose level would fall, and the person would have hypoglycaemia. If they could recognize the symptoms, they could rapidly raise the blood sugar level by eating glucose in the form of tablets, or sweets or any sugar-rich food.

SAQ 7 During exercise there is a build-up of lactate in the muscles and the bloodstream. Lactate is reconverted into pyruvate in the muscle, but the liver also takes up lactate from the bloodstream and converts it back to glycogen.

SAQ 8 A Christmas swim at Brighton is likely to be a somewhat chilly experience. The natural reaction of the body to cold would be to constrict the surface capillaries to reduce peripheral blood flow and hence heat loss. However, the over-riding effect of alcohol will be to dilate the blood vessels, allowing a greater flow of warm blood through the skin giving a pleasant feeling of warmth. The heart rate will probably increase as a result of both the exercise (swimming hard) and the shift of blood from the centre of the body to the periphery. However, the feeling of well-being would be illusory, for the body would be shunting heat away from the centre towards the skin where loss to the cold air would be rapid.

SAQ 9 (c) is the correct answer. The only reasonable deduction that can be made from the data is that the reference point in the hypothalamus is shifted in the woman with the fever. The two curves are identical apart from the set temperature at which sweating starts, which is one degree higher in the woman with the fever.

(a) No information is given about capillary size, but you should expect the capillaries to carry more blood as temperature rises. This is because the arterioles feeding the capillaries would expand.

(b) This is likely to be true, but you cannot make such a statement on the basis of the graph.

(d) There is no information about heart rate in the graph, but the slopes of the two curves are identical, which suggests that there is no difference in the rate of heat loss.

SAQ 10 Both frogs and mammals have blood that carries oxygen, lungs and a heart that circulates the blood. In the frog's heart, there is only one ventricle, whereas in mammals there are two. The consequence is that the blood in the frog ventricle is a mixture—some of it has come through the lungs, some of it has arrived via the skin. Frogs normally live in wet environments and their skin can absorb oxygen by diffusion from the wet surface through into the blood capillaries. So, the undivided ventricle of the frog is consistent with its semi-aquatic life-style. Underwater, it can obtain oxygen from the water through its skin and lungs provide no oxygen; on land drying of the skin can be tolerated as oxygen is supplied by the lungs.

INDEX FOR UNIT 23

ACKNOWLEDGEMENTS

The Course Team would like to thank David and Mary Cotterrell (University of Leeds) for their comments on a draft of this Unit, and Stewart Petersen (University of Leicester) for assistance with the TV programme.

Grateful acknowledgement is made to the following sources for permission to use material in this Unit:

Figure 6 Barrington, E. J. W., *Invertebrate Structure and Function*, 1979, Nelson and Sons; *Figure 12(b)* Keele, C. A., Neil, E. and Joels, N., *Samson Wright's Applied Physiology*, 1982, Oxford University Press.

Plate 10 Wheater, P. R., Burkitt, H. G. and Lancaster, P., *Colour Atlas of Histology*, 1985, Longmans; *Plate 11* Wellcome Institute Library, London.

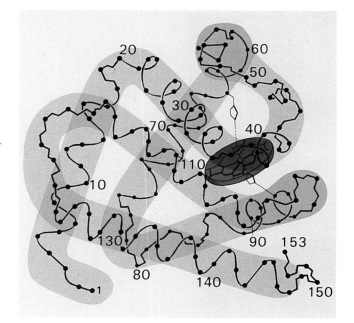

PLATE 1   The higher-order structure of myoglobin. The black dots (some of which are numbered) are amino acid residues. The blue 'folded sausage' shows the higher-order structure. Within the blue shading can be seen the primary structure coiled into several helical regions, for example, residues 126 to 147. The red disc is the oxygen-carrying haem group.

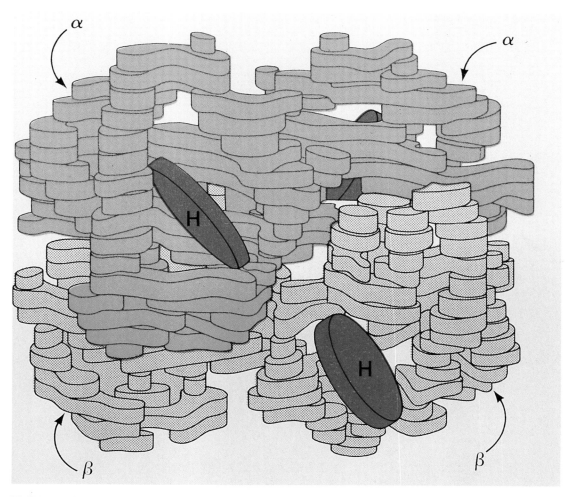

PLATE 2   A model of a haemoglobin molecule. It has a diameter of about 5 nm and a relative molecular mass of around 66 000. The α chains in this model are yellow and the β chains are blue. Three of the four haem groups (shown in red) can be seen from the angle at which the model is viewed.

PLATE 3 Colours produced in the salivary amylase experiment. Spot 1 is iodine solution plus starch solution. Spot 9 is iodine solution alone. Spot 8, obtained after $3\frac{1}{2}$ minutes in this particular experiment, is the kind of (approximate) 'no starch' end-point you should use.

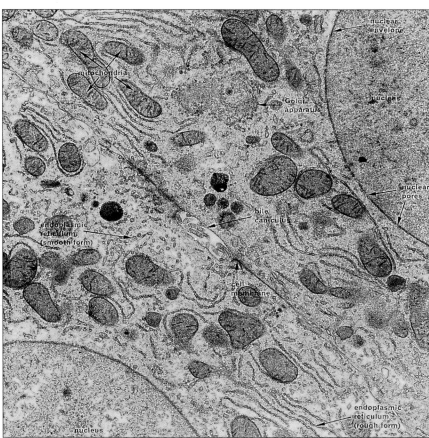

PLATE 4 Electron micrograph of two adjacent cells in rat liver; the membrane between them runs from top left to bottom right. Many mitochondria can be seen in both cells. (The Golgi apparatus and bile caniculus labelled here are both associated with the secretory functions of the liver.)
(*Magnification* ×10 000)

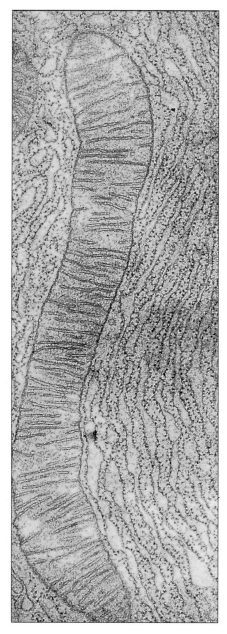

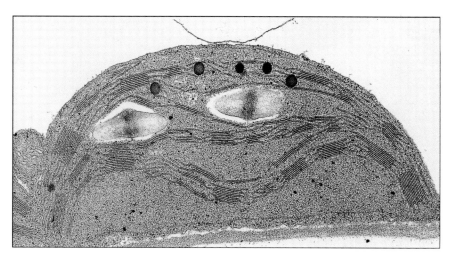

PLATE 6   Electron micrograph of a chloroplast from a leaf cell. The stacks of internal membranes are where the light stage occurs. The solution between these stacks contains the enzymes of the dark stage. The two pale, oval structures are starch grains—the temporary store of carbohydrate produced by photosynthesis. (*Magnification* ×15 500)

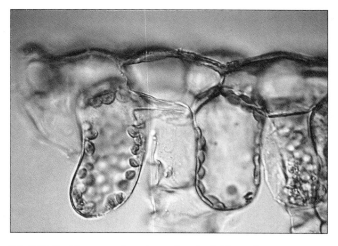

PLATE 7   Cross-section through a leaf. Note the many chloroplasts in each mesophyll cell.

PLATE 5   Electron micrograph of single mitochondrion within a mouse cell. Note the numerous folds in the inner mitochondrial membrane, and the rough endoplasmic reticulum in the surrounding cytosol. (*Magnification* ×42 000)

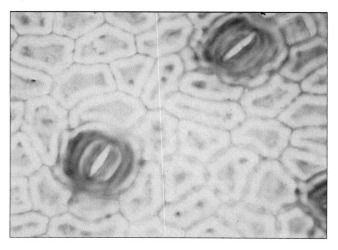

PLATE 8   Stomata: pores in the leaf epidermis through which carbon dioxide, oxygen and water vapour pass. (*Magnification* ×16 300)

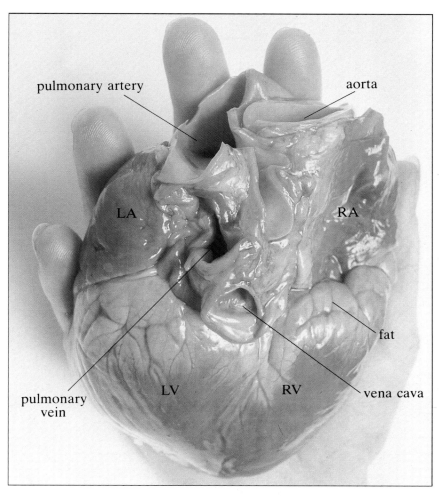

PLATE 9   Dorsal view of the heart of a pig. The diameter of the pulmonary arterial wall appears larger then usual, partly as a result of the angle of the heart and partly because the pulmonary artery had been slashed. The ventricles are foreshortened because of the angle at which the picture was taken. LA, left atrium; RA, right atrium; LV, left ventricle; RV, right ventricle. Note the cushioning layer of fat round the bottom of the heart.

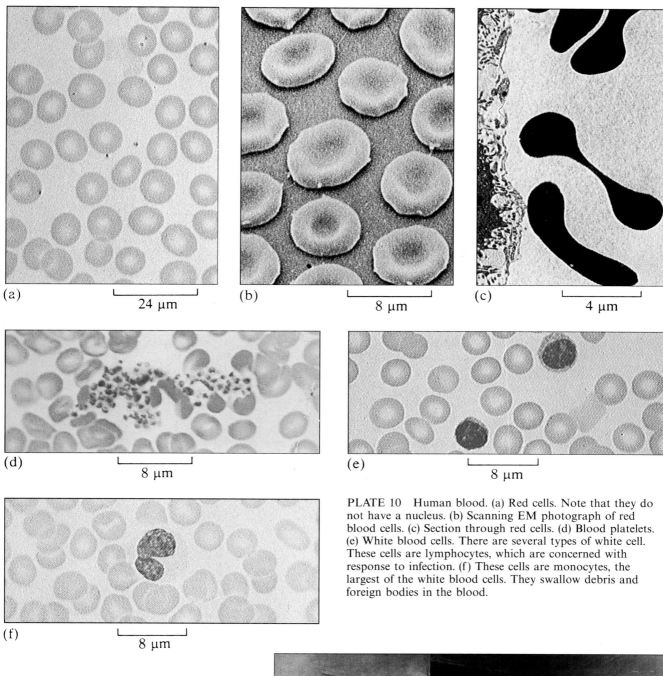

(a)

24 μm

(b)

8 μm

(c)

4 μm

(d)

8 μm

(e)

8 μm

(f)

8 μm

PLATE 10 Human blood. (a) Red cells. Note that they do not have a nucleus. (b) Scanning EM photograph of red blood cells. (c) Section through red cells. (d) Blood platelets. (e) White blood cells. There are several types of white cell. These cells are lymphocytes, which are concerned with response to infection. (f) These cells are monocytes, the largest of the white blood cells. They swallow debris and foreign bodies in the blood.

PLATE 11 The French physiologist Claude Bernard giving a practical demonstration in physiology to his pupils (oil painting by an unknown artist, in the collection in the Wellcome Institute for the History of Medicine).